# WISCONSIN...

### is my doorstep

*Also by Robert E. Gard*

*JOHNNY CHINOOK: Tall Tales and True from the
Canadian West*

# WISCONSIN
## is my doorstep

### A DRAMATIST'S YARN BOOK OF WISCONSIN LORE

by ROBERT E. GARD

Decorations by FRANK UTPATEL

LONGMANS, GREEN AND CO.
NEW YORK · LONDON · TORONTO
1948

LONGMANS, GREEN AND CO., INC.
55 FIFTH AVENUE, NEW YORK 3

LONGMANS, GREEN AND CO. LTD.
6 & 7 CLIFFORD STREET, LONDON W 1
17 CHITTARANJAN AVENUE, CALCUTTA 13
NICOL ROAD, BOMBAY 1
36A MOUNT ROAD, MADRAS 2

LONGMANS, GREEN AND CO.
215 VICTORIA STREET, TORONTO 1

WISCONSIN IS MY DOORSTEP

PUBLISHED SIMULTANEOUSLY IN
THE DOMINION OF CANADA BY
LONGMANS, GREEN AND CO., TORONTO

First Edition

Printed in the United States of America
VAN REES PRESS • NEW YORK

*For*

*MARYO*

# Author's Foreword

In imagination it is possible for an entire state to be a doorstep. This fanciful conception is aided if one travels widely and often throughout the countryside, comes to have an affection for it, hears the tales the people like to relate, and, occasionally, fabricates a tale oneself.

My Wisconsin doorstep teems with a rich and dramatic heritage of events acted by a long list of heroes and heroines, who seem to exist timelessly in a sort of dream, that Wisconsin people recognize as being essentially theirs.

Although the adventures within the dream have been told frequently, the clamor for the retelling is ceaseless; and I have no hesitation, therefore, in saying that these folktale heroes and their present-day counterparts throng often at my door. So I have set myself the task of recreating once again the drama of this place, of drawing to my door the Wisconsin players to become in my mind characters in a living fabric of legendary design.

Since the tales are mine—like everyone's—to use again, I have preserved their essential trueness, taking the liberty, only occasionally, of condensing events and adding characters to embellish the dramatic pattern. What emerges is a series of pictures sketched in my imagination as I stand in my doorway and look across my doorstep: north, where the great woods once stood; south, across the rolling farmland; west, where the Mississippi once rang with the cries of the raftsmen; east, to Michigan's shore. And in my mind I am listening, too, to the crowding characters on my doorstep telling again the yarns of the Wisconsin tradition.

# Acknowledgment

My acknowledgment and thanks are due three divisions of the University of Wisconsin: the College of Letters and Science, General Extension, and the College of Agriculture. Thanks are also due the State Historical Society of Wisconsin, Radio Station WHA, the Humanities Division of the Rockefeller Foundation.

My special thanks to A. M. Drummond, of Cornell University, who has been a pioneer in the creative use of regional materials; to Richard S. Davis, of the *Milwaukee Journal*; to Arthur S. Kimball, Robert J. Kinney, and Jonathan W. Curvin, who helped with certain yarns; and finally, to all the Wisconsin folk who have assisted in the establishment of the Wisconsin Idea Theatre and Folklore Projects.

# CONTENTS...

# Introduction

"If you want to be a Badger,
  Just come along with me,
  By the bright shining light of the moon . . ."

This siren rhyme, the source of which any good alumnus of the University of Wisconsin will readily recognize, might well serve as the introductory measure to this program of fine Wisconsin yarns. It offers just the sort of irresistible invitation to share the lore of Badgerland the pages that follow merit.

Folklore is a fascinating field of interest, not alone for the high points of the tales themselves, but for what those stories, handed down from generation to generation, tell us of the people who originated them—of their life, their attitudes, their society, their culture. European folklore has long been familiar in this country. Our vampires, werewolves, fairies, and leprechauns are all pure "furriners," though a few bonafide gremlins were unquestionably born in this country. Surely, too, Wilhelm Tell is as familiar a figure to most Americans as Paul Bunyan, for native American folklore has been a relatively neglected field until recent years. It is an interesting and hopeful fact that in the last two decades, as the nation has moved toward its present position of world leadership, there has been a notable tendency to seek the real significance of the American experiment and to re-evaluate the things that have made this nation not only great but different. We have been turning more toward ourselves and our forebears, seeking to know ourselves better, not in mere introspection but in seeking the sources of our peculiarity and our strength.

In the face of world-wide responsibility, blinking slightly in the unexpected light of the new day, we have asked ourselves somewhat incredulously how this has happened? How have we come so far so soon? In the face of the growing challenge of alien ideologies, we have had to make up our minds as to just what we have that is so different, so important, so worth our deep allegiance, so worth our ultimate sacrifice, so worth passing on to our children and to others.

We are finding the answers, as we get to know ourselves better, in the importance we rightly attribute to the individual, in our belief in equality of opportunity, in our love of contest and competition, in our melting pot of culture as well as of peoples, in our insistence that no one and nothing is above criticism, in our free schools, in our willingness to laugh at ourselves—much as we may resent others' laughing at us. And those answers have come not just from the formal studies of our political, economic, and social history but also from the folklore that sets the stage, that gives us the flavor of the America we study. For Paul Bunyan, Whiskey Johnny, and Johnny Appleseed are in their way as important to an understanding of America as

xiv

the census records—and it must be admitted that they have greater reader interest.

The author of this book is one of the younger generation who is in open revolt against the cynicism of the "forgotten generation," against the expatriate geniuses who when they looked back at all on their homeland did so unsympathetically, and against the effete literary leadership that made it unfashionable to deal with homespun subjects.

For two years he has been director of the Wisconsin Idea Theatre, a state-wide theater project which, in the image of the "Wisconsin Idea," is devoted to "a more complete general interpretation through drama of this particular part of the Middle-west; and a more complete use of the talents and materials of the region." *

This interest in Wisconsin materials, the assiduousness with which he collects them, and his appreciation of their delightful flavor, have led not only to unusual success in the Wisconsin Idea Theatre, but have put him behind the head table and on the air with a frequency which to him is no doubt alarming but which to his listeners is assurance of a good evening. They have also produced this delightful book, which, to those of us who have been following his work at the University of Wisconsin, is immediately recognizable as pure Gard.

So "if you want to be a Badger" just come along with Gard, by the bright shining light of what he probably would insist is pure Wisconsin cheese. You'll never be the same

*Gard, R. E., "The Wisconsin Idea in Theatre," Bulletin, National Theatre Conference, Vol. IX, No. 2, June 1947, p. 35.

after you get through with Bull Gordon, Gene Shepard, the Fightin' Finches and Marbert the Mad Muskellunge. Chances are, though, that you'll be a better Badger—or wish you had the luck to be one.

CLIFFORD L. LORD

State Historical Society of Wisconsin
October 27, 1947

# THINGS . . .

### on my doorstep

# CONTEST . . .

## on my doorstep

ONE day a friend of mine—an old lumberjack with a long beard—sang me a song he called "The Little Brown Bulls." * This ballad, which tells the yarn of a log skidding contest between a team of "white spotted steers" and a fabulous team o' "little brown bulls," has often been referred to as a lumberjack classic, and a true Wisconsin song.

* I have generally followed the version of "The Little Brown Bulls" as collected by Franz Lee Rickaby in *Ballads and Songs of the Shanty-Boy*. The ballad, however, contains a lapse which I have filled in with three verses for the purpose of narration.

Folks in Northern Wisconsin will mention the ballad, a few old-time lumbermen, like my friend, will even sing it for you. But about the contest itself, they are as vague as folks usually are about events around which a sort of mythology has grown. They simply say the contest was a mighty tussle, and let it go at that. A few of the more imaginative ones will tell you that they know the inside dope, and from some of the folktales—and my own imagination—I pieced together the following yarn.

It begins in the office of a boss lumberman named Mart Douglas, somewhere in the North Woods country, back— oh about 1878. Mart is sitting at his desk when Bob McClusky, a Scot, comes knocking at his door.

"Who's there?" yells Mart.

" 'Tis me, Bob McClusky."

"Come in, Bob. How are ye?"

"Fine! Fine!" roars Bob. "And have ye the skidding contract for me, Mister Douglas?"

"Well, sit down, Bob," says Mart. "You're the best skidder in Wisconsin, and . . ."

"That I am," says Bob, "an' me white spotted steers have no equal in all the woods. So if ye'll gi' me the contracts, I'll be signin' 'em."

"Now hold on, Bob," replies Mart. "It ain't as easy as that. You see, a Mr. Bull Gordon, skidder for a new outfit, called the Goliath Company, was in here this mornin'. Put up a convincin' line of talk, he did."

"Never heard o' the mon."

2

"Bull Gordon's a Yankee, McClusky. He was askin' for our skidding contract, same as you."

"Where is he?" roars Bob. "I'll be findin' him and twistin' his ears fer him. Askin' fer the contract, was he?"

"Yes, he was, Bob. And he said he could skid more logs in a season than you can, and for the same price."

"Ah," says Bob, getting up and pawing the air, "ain't it a known fact, Mister Douglas, that I'm the best skidder anywheres? And ain't it known that me white spotted steers are the best?"

"Yes," interrupts Mart. "But business is business."

"Then it's no contract you'll be gi'in me?"

"Now hold on," replies Mart. "I didn't say that. Here's what I'd like to do. I'll arrange a skidding contest between you and Bull Gordon. Are ye game, Bob?"

"You're but wastin' your time, Mister Douglas. Nobody can beat Bob McClusky. But if it's a contest you're wantin', well, bring on your Bull Gordon."

"Was hopin' you'd say yes," says Mart. " 'Twill be a mighty contest."

"And what kind o' steers is this Bull Gordon usin'?" asks Bob.

"No steers at all, Bob," Mart replies. *Bulls.* He's got a team o' *little brown bulls!*"

"What!" hollers McClusky. "Bulls! It's bulls he's drivin'?"

"We'll see," says Mart. "And now, Bob, I want you to come with me. Want you to meet Bull Gordon. Guess we'll find him at the tavern."

3

*Not a thing on the river McClusky did fear,*
*When he drew the stick o'er his big spotted steers.*
*They were young, quick, and sound, girting eight*
*    foot and three . . .*
*Says McClusky, the Scotchman, they're the laddies*
*    for me!!*

"Here's Bull Gordon, McClusky," hollers Mart, "stand·
in' over here at the bar!"

"That little feller?" scoffs McClusky. "And he's gonna
beat *me!*"

"Bull," says Mart, leading McClusky over, "want you
to meet Bob McClusky. Supposed to be the best skidder
in the State."

"Where ye from, mon?" hollers McClusky.

"State o' Maine. This feller beside me 's Kennebec
John. My helper."

"Glad to see you boys," says Kennebec.

"Gordon," McClusky says, "what do them leetle brown
bulls o' yours measure? My white spotted steers girt eight
foot and three!"

"Well, McClusky," says Gordon, "my little brown bulls
girt only six and nine."

*Bull Gordon, the Yankee, on skidding was full,*
*As he cried "whoa hush" to his little brown bulls!*
*Short-legged and soggy, girt six foot and nine.*
*Says McClusky, the Scotchman, "too light fer our*
*    pine!"*

"Bull," cries McClusky, "you're sure a sucker."

"Better explain that, Bob," says Bull.

"Why, mon, those bulls 're too light for our logs!"

"You reckon steers are better, eh?"

"Why, mon, I'll skid two to one! You know the terms o' the skid? No more 'n three logs to a thousand board feet o' lumber!"

*It's three to the thousand our contract did call.*
*Our hauling was good and the timber was tall.*
*McClusky he swore he'd make the day full,*
*An' skid two to one of the little brown bulls.*

"Want to make a little wager on your steers against my little brown bulls, Bob?" asks Bull Gordon.

"You're on, mon! What'll it be?"

"Twenty-five dollars," says Bull.

"Done," roars Bob. "And will ye pay me now?"

*"Oh no!" says Bull Gordon, "that you cannot do.*
*Though it's well we do know you've the pets of the crew!*
*And mark you, my boy, you would have your hands full*
*If you skid one more log than the little brown bulls!"*

"Now," says Bull, "what are the terms o' the contest, Mister Douglas?"

"Here are the terms, boys," says Mart. "Each outfit will work the same timberland; each of you workin' about half a mile apart. Since this is virgin timber you'll be workin', you'll each have a measured distance of at least one quarter mile to your respective skidways. You'll work one day—sunup to sunset. There'll be a referee for each one of you to see fair play. I'll furnish the scalers. They'll estimate the number of board feet of lumber in each log, and I'll furnish the judges. Winner will get a contract with my company for the season. All right?"

"All right wi' me," says McClusky.

"And with me," says Bull Gordon.

"Contest'll be one week from today."

"I'll be there," says Bob. "And say, Bull, see this here Mackinaw I'm wearin'?"

"Brightest Mackinaw I ever see, Bob," Bull replied.

"Right," says Bob, "an' I'm cuttin' this Mackinaw up, see. I'm makin' a belt from it. A belt o' victory! Fer meself, and me white spotted steers! I'll be seein' ye boys! Wi' your little brown bulls!"

*The day was appointed and soon it drew nigh*
*For twenty-five dollars their fortunes to try.*
*Both eager and anxious that morning were found*
*And scalers and judges appeared on the grounds!*

Yes, sir, the day of the contest arrived, and up there in the North woods, a considerable crowd had gathered to watch the fray. 'Twas just before sunup, and Mart Douglas was giving his last-minute instructions.

"Folks, this here'll be a skiddin' contest between Bull

Gordon, the Yankee, an' his little brown bulls, an' Bob McClusky and his white spotted steers!"

"My money's on McClusky," says one big fellow.

"Mine too," says a little fellow. "Hooray for the white spotted steers!"

"Hooray! Hooray!" yells everybody.

"Judges ready?" hollers Mart.

"Ready, Mart."

"Scalers ready?"

"Ready, Mart."

"Referees are ready, an' here comes Bob McClusky an' his white spotted steers!"

"They're the laddies fer me," hollers the big fellow. "Three cheers for McClusky!"

"Hooray! Hooray! Hooray!"

*With a hoop and a yell came McClusky in view,*
*With the big spotted steers, the pets o' the crew!*
*Both chewing their cuds—"oh boys keep your jaws*
*full!*
*You can easily beat them, the little brown bulls!"*

Then came the bulls and Bull Gordon. "Look at 'em!" yells the big fellow. "Ain't no legs to 'em! No bigger 'n dogs! Give me the white spotted steers!"

*Then out came Bull Gordon with a pipe in his jaw;*
*The little brown bulls with their cuds in their mouths.*
*And little we think when we see them come down,*
*That a hundred and forty could they jerk around!*

7

"Now boys," hollers Mart, "you know the rules. Ready, McClusky?"

"Ready an' willin'!"

"Ready, Bull Gordon?"

"Ready!"

"The sawyers and the shanty boys are gettin' your logs down! All right! Go!"

"On boys! Gee boys!" cries McClusky. "We'll fix that durned Yankee!"

*Then up spoke McClusky, come stripped to the skin!*
*"We'll dig them a hole and tumble them in!*
*We'll learn the damn Yankee to face the bold Scot!*
*We'll mix them a dose and feed it red hot!"*

*Says Gordon to Kennebec, with blood in his eye,*
*"Today we must conquer McClusky or die!"*
*Then up spoke bold Kennebec, "Boys, never fear!*
*For you n'er shall be beat by the big spotted steers!"*

*Oh, 'twas up to the logs and fasten 'em on!*
*Hurry up, boys, for it's no longer dawn!*
*The daylight is running, and if you'll take a hunch,*
*You'll hook to the logs and forget about lunch!*

*McClusky, the Scotchman, showed nothing like fear,*
*As he cried, "Whoa hush!" to the white spotted steers!*
*For it's on, boys, and gone, boys! Take hold of the*
*    snow!*
*We're hooked to the log and now let 'em go!*

*Bull Gordon he worked with a pipe in his mouth,*
*And the wind blew the smoke from the North to the*
*   South.*
*Says he to his helper, "John, I'm scared as can be*
*That those white spotted steers 're too much fer me!"*

*The sun had gone down when the foreman did say,*
*"Turn out, boys, turn out! You've enough for the day!*
*We have scaled them and counted, each man to his*
*   team,*
*And it's well we do know now which one kicks the*
*   beam!"*

So after supper was over in the camp, the crowd all
gathered in the mess hall to hear the results. Bob McClusky
had slicked all up and came carrying that belt o' victory
he'd made from his jacket.

*After supper was over McClusky appeared*
*With the belt ready made for the big spotted steers.*
*To form it he'd torn up his best Mackinaw,*
*He was bound he'd conduct it according to law!*

"Well, Mister Douglas," roars Bob, "here I be! Here's
me belt o' victory. Gi' it to me when you'll be announcin'
I've won the contest. And if ye have the contract I'll be
signin' it now. Save some time!"

"Hold on, Bob," says Mart. "Here comes Bull Gordon,
an' we must consider him, too. How do you feel, Bull?"

9

"Fine," says Bull. "But I fear me 'n my little brown bulls have lost the contest."

"So ye have," roars McClusky. "And I'm rememberin' our leetle wager. Twenty-five dollars. Hand it over!"

"Gentlemen," hollers Mart Douglas. "I'm announcin' the winner o' the skidding contest! The winner, an' the new champ, Bull Gordon!"

"Hear! Hear!" yelps McClusky. "What do ye mean, mon? Me 'n my white spotted steers musta skidded one hundred and eight. Maybe more! Mon, nothin' 'll be beatin' that!"

"McClusky," laughs Bull Gordon, "if you only skidded a hundred and eight, you only put in a half day's work! Me 'n my bulls musta skidded one hundred fifty. Maybe more!"

"Gi' me the count," bawls McClusky. "I been robbed! Cheated! Bull Gordon, I'll be breakin' ye in half! Nobody can beat McClusky an' his white spotted steers!"

"The count," says Mart, "was McClusky: one hundred an' ten. Bull Gordon: one hundred and forty!" *

*Then up spoke the scaler, "Hold on, you awhile!*
*The big spotted steers are behind just one mile!*
*For you have a hundred and ten and no more,*
*And Gordon has beat you by ten and a score!"*

"Three cheers for Bull Gordon," cries Mart.
"Hooray! Hooray! Hooray!" says the crowd.

* This refers to the number of logs skidded by each.

"Well," says Bob McClusky, "I canna understand it. But here is your twenty-five dollars, Bull. And lots o' luck may ye have wi' it!"

"Thanks, Bob," says Bull. "I'll be needin' that twenty-five dollars to marry my gal Suzy."

"Best o' luck to ye then," says Bob, "an' to your future missus. An' here! Here's my belt o' victory! Hang it on the little brown bulls! I strike me colors!"

*The shanty did ring and McClusky did swear.*
*He tore out by handfuls his long yellow hair.*
*Says he to Bull Gordon, "My colors I'll pull,*
*So here, take the belt for the little brown bulls!"*

"All right, boys," yells Mart. "And now we'll have a little celebration!"

*Here's health to Bull Gordon and Kennebec John,*
*The biggest day's work on the river they done.*
*So fill up your glasses and fill 'em up full,*
*We'll drink to the health of the little brown bulls!*

# A LADY . . .

## on my doorstep

SHE has come out of the Civil War. They call her the "Wisconsin Angel." She is small, sensitive, intelligent. There is a character about her, an undeniable purpose, a courage that her story will explain. In my mind, she is looking back over her life seeking the beginning of her tale. The beginning will be, she tells me, in the waiting room of President Abraham Lincoln's office in Washington, D. C., in the year 1863. Let's listen to her story.

12

I sat down on one of the hard chairs in Mr. Lincoln's waiting room. The crowd terrified me. Many were important men seeking political favor, carrying messages of moment. I was eager to see Mr. Lincoln, but there were others just as eager as I. One man in particular pushed his way impatiently to the secretary and said, "When can I see the President?"

"Be patient, sir," replied the secretary.

"But consarn it," the man said, "I've been waiting two hours. See here, I've a letter from Secretary-of-War Stanton. Ain't that recommendation enough?"

The secretary glanced at the letter and replied, "Yes, sir. The President will see you. You must be patient."

"I don't like to wait," said the man.

"Of course you don't, sir," the secretary said. He turned away from the man and addressed us all. "Now listen, everybody waiting to see the President! Do I have all your names?"

"You don't have mine," I said nervously, coming up to the secretary.

"No, ma'am. Your name, ma'am?"

"Harvey. Cordelia Harvey."

"Your business?"

"I bring a petition from the people of Wisconsin."

"Very well, ma'am. Be patient. The President will see you."

"I'm glad to wait," I said.

And as I sat down again I felt lonely and afraid. I sat

13

there seeking within myself the courage I needed. Suddenly it was as though I saw my entire life, a flashing dream in my nervous brain: I, Cordelia Harvey . . .

*Cordelia Perrine, a teacher in Kenosha, Wisconsin. The day she met Louis Harvey. Her happiness on her wedding day. Her pride when they elected her husband Secretary of State of Wisconsin. Her pride in 1861 when the people cheered: "Harvey! Harvey for Governor!"*

*I, Cordelia Harvey, wife of the Governor, the Civil War Governor of Wisconsin. . . Kissing him goodbye as he left one day for a trip South to visit wounded Wisconsin men in the hospitals along the Mississippi. Waiting for his return, and talking one day with my friend Mrs. Gaylord.*

*"When will the Governor return, Cordelia?"*

*I replied, "I don't know. He writes, 'Thank God for the impulse that sent me here. I have seen for myself the terrible hospital conditions endured by our men. I have done more good by coming than I can tell you.' "*

*The servant entering to tell me that Mr. Gaylord had arrived and wished to talk privately with me; my meeting with him in the hall; and my certainty, as I looked at his face, that something had happened which was to affect my entire life.*

*"There's a rumor about the Governor, Cordelia."*

*"A rumor?"*

*"More than a rumor. He's dead, Cordelia. Drowned while making a boat transfer."*

14

*Blunt finality. Death.*

*The appearance in Madison of a new Governor. Governor Salomon. My visit to him.*

*"What will you do now, Cordelia?"*

*"I desire to do something to carry on my husband's work. He was so interested in the welfare of Wisconsin men in the War. Is there not something I can do?"*

*"There is one job," said the Governor. "A woman has never before held it."*

*"What is the job, Mr. Governor?"*

*"It's the job of Sanitary Agent for the Union Hospitals. A hard, nasty job. No job for a woman."*

*"May I have the job, Mr. Governor?"*

*"Yes. The job's yours. See what you can do with it!"*

*I, Cordelia Harvey, Sanitary Agent. Walking through hospitals—mere sheds; cots so thick there was scarcely room to move between them. Disease: pneumonia, typhoid, camp fevers, the terrible diarrhea of the Southern swamps. Wounds, too. But mostly men dying of disease. The voices of the sick . . .*

| | |
|---|---|
| A Soldier: | *Let me go home! Help me go home!* |
| Another: | *Lady! Lady, help me!* |
| A Third Soldier: | *You're an angel! Take me in your chariot! Take me away! Wisconsin Angel, help me!* |
| The Surgeon: | *You better leave, ma'am. There's only disease here. Contagion. Conta-* |

gion and sympathy don't go well together, ma'am.

THE ANGEL: *Do they not, sir?*

*I, Cordelia Harvey, Wisconsin Angel, procuring needed foods for the sick. Nursing, writing letters, hearing the stories of the homesick; striving to bring a needed sympathy and gentleness to the hospitals of the South; trying with all my might to make the hospitals better places for the care of the sick. Always the voice of the young surgeon in charge, himself discouraged by the system, by the suffering.*

THE SURGEON: *You better give up, ma'am. We can't keep men alive in these River hospitals. Give it up!*

THE ANGEL: *Sir, why cannot these men be furloughed North, away from this diseased country?*

THE SURGEON: *Because it is cheaper for the Government to keep her soldiers in hospitals on the River than it is to furlough them.*

THE ANGEL: *That may be true, sir. But is it the Government's purpose to keep men alive as long as possible, or let them die for the sake of a few dollars? Many of these men could return to active service in a few weeks if they were furloughed North.*

THE SURGEON: *There are no hospitals in the North, ma'am.*

| THE ANGEL: | *Then there must be hospitals in the North.* |
| THE SURGEON: | *These men would desert if they were sent North. As long as I am in charge there will be no furloughs. Good day, ma'am.* |
| THE ANGEL: | *But the voices. The voices . . .* |
| A SOLDIER: | *Take me home!* |
| ANOTHER: | *Wisconsin Angel, help me!* |
| MANY VOICES: | *We're dying. Wisconsin Angel, help us! Send us home!* |

*Thousands of men lying in needless graves. Through my brain the thought: I will help you!*

*I, Cordelia Harvey, circulating a petition to the people of Wisconsin for the establishment of Northern hospitals; for the relief of men who were dying.*

*I, Cordelia Harvey, with the voices of Union Soldiers ringing in my ears, carrying a petition to President Lincoln in Washington. Sitting here. Waiting to see him.*

The secretary touched me on the arm. "Ma'am. Mrs. Harvey! The President will see you now."

"Thank you," I replied, and followed him into the President's office. As I went in, the President was not alone. A man was sitting across the desk from him, and as I moved forward I could hear them talking. The man was the one who, in the waiting room, had been most impatient to see the President.

**17**

THE MAN: But my nephew deserves the promotion, Mr. President. If you make him a brigadier, you may count on my continued support, sir. Yes, and the support of the people in my constituency in Pennsylvania.

LINCOLN: There are no vacancies among brigadiers. Listen my friend, let me tell you a story. Suppose you were a farmer, and that you had a cattle yard full of all sorts of cattle: cows, oxen, bulls; and you kept selling your cows and oxen, and keeping your bulls. By and by you'd find that you had nothing left but a yard full of old bulls—good for nothing under heaven. And it will be just so with my army if I don't stop making brigadier generals! Good day, sir!

THE MAN: Well . . . Good day, Mr. President.

As the man left the office, I walked slowly to Mr. Lincoln's desk. He rose to greet me. . . .

LINCOLN: Mrs. Harvey?

THE ANGEL: Yes, sir.

LINCOLN: Come and be seated, Mrs. Harvey.

THE ANGEL: Thank you, Mr. President.

LINCOLN: That man who just left . . . I told him a story. Have you heard the legend about me, Mrs. Harvey?

THE ANGEL: You mean, Mr. President, that when you tell

anyone a story, it means you refuse his
request?

LINCOLN: I have that reputation.

THE ANGEL: I trust you won't tell me a story then, Mr.
President.

LINCOLN: I knew your husband, Mrs. Harvey. I respected him. I have heard about you. Our
soldiers call you "The Wisconsin Angel."
You've done a splendid work. And now you
have come to me with a request for military
hospitals in the North.

THE ANGEL: Yes, Mr. President. The need for such
hospitals . . .

LINCOLN: Wait. The matter seems settled to me.
Our medical officers refuse to recommend
Northern hospitals.

THE ANGEL: Mr. President, many, many soldiers in our
western army on the Mississippi River must
have Northern air or die. There are thousands of graves all along our Southern rivers
for which the Government is responsible—
ignorantly, doubtless—but this ignorance
must not continue. If you will send these sick
men North, you will have ten men where
you have one now.

LINCOLN: If these men are sent North they will desert.
So where is the difference?

THE ANGEL: Dead men cannot fight; and they cannot
desert.

**19**

LINCOLN: You propose a fine way to decimate the army, Mrs. Harvey. We should never get a man of them back. Not one.

THE ANGEL: If you believe that, Mr. Lincoln, then I don't believe you know our people. The common soldiers are the chief sufferers, and they are the most loyal.

LINCOLN: Your opinion, unfortunately, Mrs. Harvey, is unsupported by the facts. How many men, Mrs. Harvey, do you suppose the Government was paying in the Army of the Potomac at the Battle of Antietam, and how many men do you suppose could actually be obtained for battle at the time?

THE ANGEL: I don't know.

LINCOLN: This war might have been finished at that time, had every man been in his place. Out of one hundred and seventy thousand men— which the Government was paying, Mrs. Harvey—only eighty-three thousand could be obtained for action. We nearly lost the war.

THE ANGEL: The missing men, Mr. President, were certainly not in Northern hospitals. Because there were none. You have made no argument against Northern hospitals.

LINCOLN: I am a busy man, Mrs. Harvey. Go and see the Secretary of War. Here, I'll give you a note to him.

THE ANGEL: Thank you, Mr. Lincoln.

LINCOLN:    Here's the note to Secretary-of-War Stanton.

THE ANGEL: May I . . . return to you, Mr. Lincoln?

LINCOLN:    Yes. You may return.

THE ANGEL: Thank you, Mr. Lincoln.

I, Cordelia Harvey, walking to Mr. Stanton's office. My feet dragging. My cause hopeless.

"This way, Mrs. Harvey. Mr. Stanton will see you now. This way, please."

"Mrs. Harvey?" asked Secretary-of-War Stanton as I passed into his office and took the chair he held for me.

"I'm Cordelia Harvey," I replied.

"Mrs. Harvey," began Mr. Stanton, pacing about the room, "you are urging the establishment of Northern hospitals. You say our River hospitals are dirty and unfit."

"So they are, Mr. Stanton," I said.

"Madam," said Mr. Stanton, stopping beside his desk and fumbling among his papers, "in President Lincoln's note to me he says 'Listen to this lady. She talks sense.' But, madam, you are not talking sense. We have had the hospitals inspected time after time; always the reports are good!"

"Naturally," I said.

"How do you mean 'naturally'?" he asked sharply.

"I mean the medical officers know the authorities don't want hospitals established so far from the army lines, and they report accordingly."

"That can't be true, Mrs. Harvey."

21

"It is true, Mr. Stanton."

"I assure you, Mrs. Harvey," he said, "that the Surgeon General is on a tour of inspection right now."

"Yes," I replied, "and his report will be: Hospitals satisfactory."

"I can do nothing until the Surgeon General returns," said Mr. Stanton reseating himself. "Good day, Mrs. Harvey."

"Good day, Mr. Stanton," I said.

I left his office and walked back to report to President Lincoln.

I spoke to the secretary. "The President is busy, ma'am."

"Thank you," I said. "I'll wait until he's free."

"Just be seated, ma'am."

I waited for an hour. The steady stream of persons through the office made it seem impossible that I should ever see the President again. I arose from my chair; approached the secretary. "He is still busy, ma'am. He'll be busy for some time."

"I'll wait then."

After I had waited another hour, the secretary told me that the President was free for a moment and would see me. "Don't stay long, please," cautioned the secretary.

"I won't."

The President was standing at the window and turned as I entered.

LINCOLN:    Come in, Mrs. Harvey. What did the Secretary of War say?

THE ANGEL: Mr. Stanton refuses to take any action until the Surgeon General returns. Mr. Lincoln, I have nowhere else to go except to you.

LINCOLN: If you wait for the return of the Surgeon General, you'll wait a long time. He won't return to Washington for three months. Would you wait that long?

THE ANGEL: I'll remain in Washington until I get what I came here for, Mr. Lincoln. I believe in the final perseverence of the Saints.

The President laughed, came to me, took my arm, and escorted me to the door. "I'll speak to the Secretary of War myself," he said. "Come back in the morning."

"Thank you, Mr. Lincoln," I replied.

I walked home to my hotel convinced that I had lost the fight. What could I do after all—a lonely woman against the greatest odds? I passed a restless night, arose early the next morning, walked back to Mr. Lincoln's crowded office.

"Be seated, Mrs. Harvey," said the secretary. "The President is busy."

*The President is busy. The President is busy. The President is busy. And men dying. Dying. Dying.*

"Be seated, Mrs. Harvey, please."

The evening before the President had seemed quite cheerful for a moment; but now this morning he was completely different. He seemed angry. Almost sullen. His first words to me were like a challenge.

23

LINCOLN:     Well, Mrs. Harvey?

THE ANGEL:   Well, Mr. Lincoln?

LINCOLN:     Have you nothing to say, Mrs. Harvey?

THE ANGEL:   Nothing, Mr. President, until I hear your decision. You asked me to come this morning. Have you decided?

LINCOLN:     This idea about Northern hospitals is a great humbug! I'm tired of hearing about it!

THE ANGEL:   Mr. Lincoln, you are overwhelmed with care and responsibility. I would rather have stayed at home than to have added to your burden, but . . .

LINCOLN:     I wish you *had* stayed at home!

THE ANGEL:   Mr. President, nothing would have given me greater pleasure. But a keen sense of duty to this Government, justice and mercy to its most loyal supporters, and regard for your honor and position made me come. The people can't understand why their friends are left to die, when with proper care they might live and do good for their country. Mr. Lincoln, I believe you will be grateful for my coming.

LINCOLN:     Is that what you think, Mrs. Harvey?

THE ANGEL:   It is.

LINCOLN:     I have just finished talking with a person who wants me to spare the life of a deserter. Madam . . .

THE ANGEL:   But I am not pleading for the lives of crimi-

nals or deserters, Mr. President, nor for
those who are in the least disloyal. I come
to plead for those who were the first to come
to the aid of this Government, who helped to
place you where you are because they trusted
you. These men have done all they could.
And even now, with their health gone, they
still pray for your life and the life of this
Republic. I know, Mr. President, that a
majority of these sick men would live again
if they might be sent North.

LINCOLN:    You assume to know more than I do.

THE ANGEL: Mr. President, you must pardon me. I meant
no disrespect. But sir, it is because of this
knowledge—because I *do* know things you
do not know—that I come to you. If you
knew what I know about hospital conditions,
and will do nothing about it, Mr. President,
then the American people have trusted you
for nothing. If you believe me, you will give
me Northern hospitals. If not . . .

LINCOLN:    You assume to know more than the surgeons
do. . . .

THE ANGEL: No, sir. I don't pretend to have medical
knowledge. And I don't come here for your
favor . . . I'm not an aspirant for military
honor. I'm merely here to state facts. Mr.
Lincoln, the medical authorities know that
you're opposed to the establishment of

25

Northern hospitals, and they report to please you—yes, to win your favor. They make a casual tour of inspection—cigars in their mouths, rattans in their hands; they talk to the surgeon in charge of the price of cotton; they abuse our generals for not performing their duty better; and finally those inspectors come out into the open air, take a deep breath as though escaping from suffocation, and say, "Sir, you have a very fine hospital here. The boys seem to be doing very well. Perhaps a little more attention to ventilation is desirable!"

Mr. Lincoln! I come from no such casual tour! I have visited the regimental hospitals from Quincy to Vicksburg, and I come to you from the cots of men who have died— yes who might have lived, had you permitted! This is a hard thing to say, sir, but it's true.

LINCOLN: You are speaking of Wisconsin regimental hospitals?

THE ANGEL: Yes. My work has been largely with Wisconsin men.

LINCOLN: Wisconsin sent me fifty thousand men. (*Angrily*) Madam, I've a good mind to dismiss every Wisconsin man from the service! Have no more trouble with them!

THE ANGEL: Mr. President, you don't mean that!

LINCOLN: No. I don't.

THE ANGEL: If you will grant my petition, you will be glad as long as you live. These grateful hearts will give you strength.

LINCOLN: (*Sadly*) I shall never be glad any more.

THE ANGEL: You will be glad, Abraham Lincoln, when the War is over. When the Government is restored, who will have more reason to be glad than you?

LINCOLN: The springs of life are wearing away. The people do not realize the magnitude of this rebellion. It will be a long time before the end.

THE ANGEL: Have you decided to refuse my petition, Mr. President?

LINCOLN: I've decided nothing. I thought I had made up my mind, but apparently not. Come again tomorrow at twelve. There's a Cabinet meeting, but we should be through by twelve o'clock. Good day, Mrs. Harvey.

THE ANGEL: Good day, Mr. President.

I, Cordelia Harvey, talking as I talked to President Abraham Lincoln. I, a nobody, champion of a lost cause; walking back to my dismal room; feeling more empty and unhappy than I had ever felt; shedding womanish tears, too. Futile tears.

And then the morning: walking, walking back to Mr. Lincoln's office. Afraid to see him again, but forcing myself

27

to go. As I went into his waiting room I heard the clock strike twelve. People crowded as usual to see the President. Everyone with a request. So many requests. The secretary called suddenly, "Attention! Attention everyone waiting to see the President! The President will see no one today."

"But I say," cried a man waiting near me, "my instructions are specific. My affairs can't wait."

"The President will see no one," droned the secretary. "Cabinet meeting." He looked over the crowd a moment, then he called, "Is Mrs. Cordelia Harvey present?"

I replied, "Yes. Here I am."

"Oh, Mrs. Harvey," said the secretary, "the President desires you to wait."

"Thank you," I said. I sat down. I heard the clock strike one, and I thought: I have failed. More waiting. Two o'clock. I arose and asked the secretary, "Are you *sure* that I am to wait?"

"The President desires you to wait, Mrs. Harvey."

At three o'clock the secretary called to me, "Mrs. Harvey, the Cabinet has adjourned."

A few moments later President Lincoln crossed the room toward me. His face: bone, nerve, muscle so plainly seen. A tall man. A tired man. An awkward man.

LINCOLN:     I'm sorry to have kept you waiting, Mrs. Harvey. The Cabinet has only this minute adjourned.

THE ANGEL:  My waiting doesn't matter. You're tired, Mr. Lincoln. We needn't talk today.

28

LINCOLN: Mrs. Harvey, I only wished to tell you that an order equivalent to the establishment of a large hospital in your State has been issued nearly twenty-four hours!

THE ANGEL: Mr. President, I . . . Mr. Lincoln . . .

LINCOLN: Why, madam, you're weeping! What's the matter? Doesn't the news make you happy?

THE ANGEL: I was so sure I'd failed, Mr Lincoln. I . . . I thank you in the name of thousands who will bless you for this act!

LINCOLN: Why, ma'am, you put your case so well, I couldn't have done anything else. I want you to come here again tomorrow at nine. I'll give you a copy of the order. Will you come?

And so it was I, Cordelia Harvey, champion of a successful cause. Sick with joy and excitement! So sick I arrived at the White House at eleven o'clock instead of nine the next morning. The secretary was calling my name.

"Cordelia Harvey! Mrs. Cordelia Harvey!"

"I'm late!" I gasped as I rushed to him. "I'm very sorry. I was ill. You see . . ."

"The President will see you immediately," said the secretary disapprovingly. "This way, Mrs. Harvey."

The President was indeed waiting for me, and he was smiling.

LINCOLN: Good morning, Mrs. Harvey. Come, sit down.

THE ANGEL: Mr. President, I'm late. Forgive me. I was ill last night . . .

**29**

LINCOLN: Did joy make you ill?

THE ANGEL: It must have been joy.

LINCOLN: What would you have done had I refused your request, Mrs. Harvey? You'd have been angry, of course.

THE ANGEL: Mr. President, if you'd refused, I would have been neither sick nor angry.

LINCOLN: What would you have done?

THE ANGEL: I would have been here at *nine o'clock*, Mr. Lincoln!

The President laughed. "Mrs. Harvey, I shall name this first hospital for you."

"Mr. Lincoln, could you," I said, "would you name it instead for my husband?"

"Of course," said Mr. Lincoln. "It will be called the *Louis Harvey Hospital*."

"You've been so kind to me, Mr. Lincoln."

Mr. Lincoln chuckled. "You almost think me handsome now, don't you?"

"Mr. Lincoln, to me you are perfectly lovely!"

We laughed together, and he took my hand. "Goodbye, Wisconsin Angel."

"Goodbye, Mr. Lincoln. God bless you."

# DUEL . . .

## on my doorstep

THE legend carried on Wisconsin automobile license plates—"America's Dairyland"—has not achieved its conspicuous position by chance. There was a time when Wisconsin ranked high as a wheat-growing state. Then the land grew less able to produce bumper crops of wheat, and Wisconsin farmers turned to dairying.

"America's Dairyland" has a long background of dairymen's feuds with the butterine and filled-cheese interests, of the development of a butterfat test by a University of

31

Wisconsin scientist, Stephen Moulton Babcock, that revolutionized the dairy industry, and of the development of a high regard for pure-bred dairy cattle.

These days Wisconsin produces a large share of the nation's milk and cheese, and if you go into, say, Monroe, in Southern Wisconsin, you will find that predominantly Swiss community very conscious of its chief means of livelihood. I mean, specifically, cheese making.

One day when I was in Monroe I heard a yarn that demonstrates how jealously the cheese tradition is guarded. As background I better say that Monroe has long been famous for its various makes of cheese, among which Limburger has held an esteemed position.

In the early days of Monroe those citizens, not so fond of cheese, held their noses when the big wagons loaded with Limburger passed through the town; some citizens even demanded that the cheese wagons discover some other route to their destination than that around Monroe's town square.

However, with the increasing prosperity brought about by cheese, the odor of Limburger became respected—even hailed with delight—and disparaging remarks were almost unheard of, until one day in 1935.

On this January day Monroe's postmaster, John Burkhard, sat in his office, basking in, and perhaps warmed by, the golden era and aura of Monroe cheese when suddenly an assistant entered bearing a package.

"John, look!" cried the assistant shaking with excitement.

32

"What's wrong?" asked Mr. Burkhard, reaching across his desk to spread a cracker with golden Limburger.

"This package!" cried the assistant. "This package of Limburger sent to Independence, Iowa, by the Badger-Brodhead Cheese Company. It's been returned to us by the Independence postmaster."

"For what reason?" said Mr. Burkhard.

"For the reason," shouted the assistant, "that it smells too bad to keep in the post office. In fact, Postmaster Miller writes that this package of Limburger made one of his rural carriers so sick he was laid up for several days!"

"Let me smell the package," Mr. Burkhard said. He took the package of cheese and sniffed it carefully. "I can discern no odor whatever. Can you?"

"There's a bit of fragrance about it," said the assistant. "But why not? It's Limburger! The King of the Cheeses!"

"Exactly," said Mr. Burkhard getting up and pacing around his office. "Limburger asks no odds of anyone. It creates its own exclusive atmosphere."

"It may be," said the assistant, though probably not believing what he said, "that there are some who don't exactly like the odor of Limburger."

"Green County folks," said Mr. Burkhard solemnly, "don't value books for their covers, people for their faces, nor good cheese for its smell. Return the package to Postmaster Miller immediately."

"Okay, John," said the assistant.

So a short time passed and one day the package returned again to the Monroe post office. "Postmaster Miller, of

Independence, Iowa, says," stated the assistant, "that he has returned the package as unfit for delivery and trusts that we will dispose of it."

"He does?" cried Mr. Burkhard. "That's almost treason! Send my secretary in here!" And when the secretary was ready, Mr. Burkhard dictated a stout reply to Postmaster Miller. "Limburger," he stated, "has every constitutional right to travel through the U. S. mails. You, sir, are un-doubtedly lacking in esthetic values."

The reply, of course, was duly received. The Iowa postmaster, who proved to be a former newspaper editor, was able to retort in kind.

"You mean *anesthetic values*," he countered, "and I am fully appreciative, if you please."

"This," said Mr. Burkhard reflectively to his staff, "has gone far enough. It's a matter for Washington. If Limburger can't travel through the mails our whole civilization is on the rocks. Take a letter!" he said to his secretary. "Take a letter to Postmaster General Jim Farley in Washington. He'll settle this fast enough!"

So off went the letter to James Farley in Washington, and back came his reply: "I'm sorry," he wrote to Mr. Burkhard, "but at this distance I can't tell whether the cheese smells bad or not."

"We'll fix that," said Mr. Burkhard. "Do up a package of Limburger and send it to Mr. Farley. Let him decide for himself."

And off went a carefully done up package of Limburger to Washington. For a time nothing was heard. Then word came in a roundabout manner. Jim Farley was himself under attack by Huey Long, and the newspapers saw in the cheese situation opportunity for a few humorous remarks. One editor wrote:

"Green County, Wisconsin, Limburger, has at last accomplished what Huey Long has not succeeded in doing—getting Postmaster Jim Farley out of his comfortable office."

John Burkhard, naturally, refused to believe this nonsense. "Certainly," he cried, "there must be somebody in Washington with a normal sense of smell. We'll contact the second and third assistant Postmasters General."

Meanwhile the newspaper wits continued to have a field day. "Jim Farley is facing a strong issue," commented a New York paper. "What a day for hydrogen sulphide," added another.

In Iowa, Postmaster Miller remained firm. "Limburger shall not pass!" he cried. "The U. S. Postal Service has withstood many attacks. But it has never *smelled!*"

John Burkhard's faith in home industry, however, was to receive reward. A letter arrived from the second assistant Postmaster General, Harlee Branch, in Washington. "I have carefully sniffed the package of Limburger cheese you sent to this office," he wrote to Mr. Burkhard. "It has no offensive odor. In fact, has no odor unless held directly under the nostrils. You have wrapped this cheese in wax paper, tin foil, brown wrapping paper, and heavy paper on the outside. Wrapped in this manner you have the authority of this office to send Limburger through the mails. To my

35

knowledge, Postmaster Miller, of Independence, Iowa, is the only one who has complained."

"The battle is over!" cried Mr. Burkhard. "Long live Limburger!" And then he became solemn. "There is, however," he reflected, "one person in the country who has not been converted to an affection for this wonderful cheese: Postmaster Miller, of Iowa. Something must be done immediately!"

After thinking the matter over, Mr. Burkhard decided to challenge Mr. Miller to a duel. A cheese-sniffing duel. "I will meet you at the St. Julien Hotel in Dubuque," he wired, "on Saturday, March ninth. I'll bring the lunch, and that means the best Limburger in Green County, to convince you to the belief that Limburger is actually a fine dairy product, not to be discriminated against because of smell."

Mr. Miller, who was equally eager to do battle, accepted. His telegram read: "If Julien objects, strongly suggest contest be held in tannery. No smells barred. Winner takes all. Limburger has no terrors for me since I lost my sense of smell ten years ago, but Monroe seems wrapped up in it. I take it each man furnishes his own weapons."

The entire cheese industry waxed jubilant over the ensuing publicity. "Cheese-sniffing duel of the century to be held," screamed the headlines. The radio commentators and the comedy programs took up the farce. Orders for Limburger poured into Monroe. John Burkhard was the hero of the day. "I am hopeful that this publicity will be the turning point in the Limburger cheese industry," stated

36

one official; and the newspapers gleefully recalled that affairs of honor were usually held in the morning, but because Dubuque was approximately half-way between Monroe and Independence, and each duelist would need to drive about seventy miles, the duel would be held at 2:30 P.M.

Mr. Burkhard, fearful that Mr. Miller could not withstand the terrific ordeal, assembled an old gas mask, a spring clothespin, and smelling salts in case of an Iowa emergency.

"We will win!" said Mr. Burkhard. "We must win for the honor of Monroe cheese!"

Reporters swarmed to the scene, and many colorful accounts of the meeting were given. Perhaps the best of these was written by a *Milwaukee Journal* man, Richard S. Davis:

The correspondent is sending this dispatch from the dueling grounds: Parlor B in the Hotel St. Julien, Dubuque. On every hand is evidence of the historic contest between Chevalier J. J. Burkhard, Postmaster of Monroe, Wisconsin, and Leftenant W. F. Miller, Acting Postmaster of Independence, Iowa. It has been a duel to the breath and everywhere is spent ammunition.

It was Leftenant Miller, away back there in January, who voiced the insult to Mlle. Limburger. He said bluntly that she smelled bad, and that he would not longer permit her to hang around the post office. He said, moreover, that she was improperly dressed and that she was contaminating the less flamboyant parcels in the vault.

Mlle. Limburger was sent back in disgrace to Monroe from whence she came. But again she ventured into the office of the sensitive Leftenant Miller and again she was ordered out as a wanton and malodorous baggage. The second affront occurred February 28.

This was altogether too much for the gallant Chevalier Burkhard. He challenged Leftenant Miller to a duel to be fought hand to hand with rye bread sandwiches, on neutral ground. The place was Dubuque, and the hour was 2:30 P.M. Saturday. The appointed moment coincided nicely with lunchtime. The contestants were on time to the second.

The injured party, Chevalier Burkhard, appeared with a considerable company of Monroe citizens with Colonel Ralph H. Wenger, of the Badger-Brodhead Cheese Company, as chief second. Leftenant Miller was accompanied only by his two sons and J. H. Levin, of the Post Office Construction Department. Major Levin acted as second for the independent gentleman from Independence.

Neither contestant wore armor of any sort, except an opulent napkin placed immediately below the second chin. Both were standing stoically as they advanced to shake hands. A hush fell upon the gathering of Monroe, Independence, and Dubuque citizens, flanked by the correspondents and photographers who had been tipped off on the date.

The formalities over, Chevalier Burkhard drew his knife and cut a thick slice of Badger Brand. He placed the aromatic ammunition upon a slice of rye and thrust it into the dauntless right hand of Leftenant Miller. General

38

Anton F. Schrup, Postmaster of Dubuque who was serving as referee, spoke the signal that had been agreed upon: "Allons, Messieurs," said General Schrup. "Go to it!"

Leftenant Miller took a large and manful bite. His grim expression changed. He took another bite and a smile appeared on his ruddy countenance. He took a third bite which meant the end of the sandwich, and his battle-scarred face turned positively beatific.

In the meantime Chevalier Burkhard had been loading again, and when Leftenant Miller completed the final swallow, another charge was given him point-blank. Again he took it full in the mouth, and again he gave every evidence of full enjoyment. It was apparent that this would be the most one-sided duel in history.

A third time Chevalier Burkhard loaded and fired with perfect aim. A third time Leftenant Miller took three bites—making nine bites in all—and the cheese disappeared beneath his waistcoat.

The Independence traducer then held up his hand in token of surrender. He was still smiling broadly, but looked a trifle dry. He moved slowly to the center of Parlor B where many bottles containing restoratives had been placed in case of casualties, and proposed a toast to his conqueror.

"Chevalier Burkhard," he said, "your honor, and the honor of your girl friend, Mlle. Limburger, is avenged. I pledge my word that never again will I say or do anything to reflect upon either of you. Chevalier and Gentlemen, I give you a cheese that is a cheese!"

All the tenseness of the occasion disappeared with Leftenant Miller's acknowledgment of defeat. Onlookers who had been holding their ears, if not their noses, promptly relaxed, and the rest of the meeting was nothing if not jovial.

A good many of the bottles on the table in Parlor B contained the famous liquid companion of Mlle. Limburger, Herr Pilsener. The two were the life of the party. Even Leftenant Miller was never without one or the other on his lap.

Further to add to the triumph of Mlle. Limburger, Chevalier Burkhard and Chief Second Wenger spoke eulogies to the "living cheese." Both eloquent gentlemen declared that every other variety is a sissy. They lauded the scent of Mlle. Limburger, her beauty of complexion, and her firm yellow body. It was enough to bring blushes to any heroine.

"The reason Mlle. Limburger bears her own perfume," said Chief Second Wenger, "is just this: Within her tender skin—rind to you roughnecks—is whey. The whey ferments and that makes the aroma. It is just a natural process like the distilling of perfume within the rose. Other cheeses don't have Mlle. Limburger's fragrance because they lack whey."

Then he discoursed on the garments worn by Mlle. Limburger when she journeys through the mails. No fashionable lady has such lingerie. First there is parchment, then manilla, then tin foil, then a filmy label, then

40

a wax-paper wrapper, and finally a parchment coat in lieu of mink.

"In lieu of mink," murmured Leftenant Miller, "to retain the—that is, er—I mean to retain the unsurpassed fragrance."

"Precisely," said Chief Second Wenger.

But all the same, the other Chief Second, Major Levin, of the Post Office Construction Corps, took the correspondent aside. He said: "We are now building a new post office in Independence. It will be a modern and beautiful edifice."

"What will be its special feature?" asked the correspondent.

Major Levin paused and smiled. Then he said impressively, "A smell-proof vault."

Henceforth when Mlle. Limburger arrives from Monroe, Wisconsin, she will be royally received in Independence, Iowa. It's a grand idea for a lady so renowned.

# WEATHER . . .

## on my doorstep

THE weather on my doorstep is mighty uncertain. At least folks in Wisconsin'll tell you that. Not that they *dislike* Wisconsin weather; they'll point with pride to an especially deep snow or low temperature, or tell you that Wisconsin has the longest series of bright, clear winter days you'll find anywhere. The general trend of their remarks, though, is that Wisconsin weather is interesting. It keeps a fellow guessing.

The subject came up one day in a class I was teaching

at the University. I posed a question: "What is the most important topic of conversation in the world?"

"War, maybe," said a young lady.

"The destiny of man, perhaps," said a young man.

"Management versus labor?" asked a boy.

"Love, maybe?" asked a girl.

The class thought the last answer an especially good one.

"I tell you what I think, Professor," said one of the brighter young men. "I think the most important topic of conversation in the world is the weather. Especially Wisconsin weather."

"What do you know about Wisconsin weather?" I asked.

"I don't know much about it. Doubt if anybody does. But Wisconsin weather's an important topic to me. You see, I live here in Madison, and my girl lives about thirty-five miles north: up in Baraboo. Naturally I drive up there quite a bit. Never make that trip without wondering what kind of weather's going to hit me. Man, I'd sure like to be able to forecast the weather in Wisconsin! I'd sure like to be able to get right up there in the sky and find out just *why* Wisconsin weather's so unpredictable. I sure would."

"All right," I said, "let's suppose, just for the fun of it, that there is an old fellow who lives up in the sky over Wisconsin, turnin' the water on and off, sendin' the winds and the snows. Let's suppose that this old fellow is up there right now and hearin' your wish about knowin' the weather. Guess he'd talk somethin' like this:

**43**

WEATHER KING: Sure! I've heard men dream like that for twenty, thirty, forty . . . can't rightly recall how many thousand years! Feel sorry for 'em! You see, I'm the old fellow who lives up here in the sky. Call me the Weather King, if you want to. Or call me winds, pressure areas, clouds, currents, heat, cold, snow, sleet, hail. Call me rainfall, rainfall near the margin, average rainfall. I'm all of those things. And say, folks, I hear more squawks per day than any bein'—human or otherwise—in this whole universe! Got a tough job! Men call me some mighty hard names! Listen! Hear 'em?

A MAN: Ain't this Wisconsin weather horrible?

A WOMAN: Deepest snow Wisconsin's had for thirty years. Can't even *see* Milwaukee!

A MAN: When is this fickle weather gonna stop?

WEATHER KING: You see? There they go, callin' me fickle again. Well, if you had to set up here in the sky for a hundred million years, bein' insulted a good share of that time, you'd be fickle too, I bet. Have to bust loose once in a while just to keep my sense of humor! 'Course, my job does have some advantage, at that. Sitting up here in the Wisconsin sky I can see everything that goes on there below. Some of the things I see amuse me. Like the songs they sing about me: blue sky, gray sky, silver linin', 'tain't gonna rain . . . And these young fellers that pretend to make a study of the signs o' the weather! Only yesterday I heard a young feller down at Madison town givin' a lecture to a bunch of ladies on weather signs. He was sayin' . . .

LECTURER: Ladies of the Wisconsin Green Fingers Society, I have chosen as the subject of my address: "Some Weather Signs."

1ST LADY: Interesting. I know some myself.

2ND LADY: So do I.

LECTURER: Ever since man first put his hand to tilling the soil, he has speculated each spring about the prospects of his harvest. When snows begin to melt, even his wife and children join him in watching for the portents of the coming season. You may, in the spring, after an especially heavy winter of snow, hear the Wisconsin farmer quote this old proverb . . .

1ST LADY: I know that one. "A year of snow, a year of plenty!"

LECTURER: Thank you, madam. You took the words right out of my mouth. Well, here are some other Wisconsin proverbs that derive from the scientific fact that a

45

winter of heavy snow delays the blossoming of fruit trees until after the normal period of killing frosts: . . .

1ST LADY: "January blossoms fill no man's cellar."

2ND LADY: "A February spring is worth nothing."

3RD LADY: "March damp and warm does farmer much harm." You see, Mr. Lecturer, we ladies do know our Wisconsin weather sayings.

1ST LADY: Mr. Lecturer . . .

LECTURER: Yes, madam?

1ST LADY: It's true, isn't it, that when my corns ache and my joints are stiff, there's going to be a storm?

LECTURER: Well, madam, I'm sorry to disappoint you, but the fact is that aching corns are usually caused by the expanding and contracting of shoe leather according to the degree of humidity; which, of course, might occasionally be indicative of . . .

1ST LADY: Why, I can't believe you. My corns always ache before a storm!

LECTURER: That may be, madam, but . . .

2ND LADY: Ladies of the Green Fingers Society, I think I have something to add to what our brilliant lecturer has already said. I have made a detailed study of weather signs as they are observed in our native state:

> When woodpeckers are noisy
> When swallows are flying low,
> When the sun shines through a watery
> haze,
> And there's a halo around the moon—
> also,
> There'll be bad weather.

There'll be a long winter if the bears retire to their hibernating dens earlier; if muskrats build their houses taller; if ducks fly in a U instead of a V. There'll be bad weather if a cat licks her fur against the grain, or washes her face over her ears, or sits with her tail to the fire.

LECTURER: Madam, I assure you . . .

2ND LADY: Before a storm sheep will frisk about and butt each other; dishes will sweat and horses will sweat in the stable.

LECTURER: Really, madam, if you will let me . . .

2ND LADY: If the breastbone of a goose is white, there will be much snow. But if the breastbone is covered with red spots, there will be a hard winter; but if there are only a few red spots, the winter will be mild.

LECTURER: Very true, madam, but let me explain . . .

2ND LADY: Everybody everywhere says:

> Evening red and morning gray
> Are tokens of a bonnie day.

47

LECTURER: Yes. That's because a red evening means there is no moisture . . .

2ND LADY: But: Evening gray and morning red
Will bring down rain upon your head.

LECTURER: Of course! A red morning implies moisture . . .

1ST LADY: My mother used to say when there was a storm coming:
I know ladies by the score
Whose hair, like seaweed, scents the storm;
Long, long before it starts to pour,
Their looks assume a baleful form!
And now, let's give a vote of thanks to our speaker. And since my corns are beginning to *really* hurt, let's all get our umbrellas and adjourn!

WEATHER KING: Yes, they've been tryin' to figure me out for a long, long time. The Wisconsin Indian has been figurin' on me for centuries!

INDIAN: Geese fly high means late fall. Geese fly low means storm coming. When crows disappear sure sign real winter at hand. Crows disappear in spring several days before storm. Hornets, bees, build high nests means deep snow—hard winter.

Weasels and rabbits get white early, means long, hard winter.

WEATHER KING: And a whole lot of the Wisconsin folks set store by ground-hog day. Just listen to what that girl's sayin' down there at Portage on the Wisconsin River:

GIRL: If ground-hog day is fair and bright, Winter must take another flight.

If ground-hog day brings storm and rain, Winter is gone and will not come again.

WEATHER KING: And there's a fellow over at Eau Clair ... What's he sayin'?

EAU CLAIR MAN: I would rather see my wife upon her bier

Than see ground-hog day clear.

WEATHER KING: 'Course, the weather experts have me figured out pretty close these days. They know I send the most cold up in the Northwest part of the State . . . around Spooner, Winter, or Barron, maybe. Depends on how I feel. I send the most heat over along the Mississippi River. Prairie du Chien, sometimes, I warm up pretty good!

Send the most wind over around Superior, and I guess most rain around the North-Central part. Yep, those experts are pretty good at guessin' what I'm up

**49**

to. But even experts can guess wrong! There's a story they like to tell in a small Wisconsin town up Stevens Point way. Happened right after the war was over. You see, I was hoverin' over a farmhouse where a youngster lived. A girl. 'Bout nine or ten, maybe. And I heard this youngster talkin' to her Ma.

"Mother," says the girl.

"Yes, Mary?"

"Read me daddy's letter again."

Well that mother'd already read the letter thirty or forty times, but she took it out again and read it to the young lady. Went somethin' like this:

"My Dearest: Don't think it's a false alarm this time. Near as I can figure I'll be home Sunday mornin' on that bus that gets into town about seven o'clock. Will get Jim at the garage to drive me out. I guess you know what this means to me, or maybe you don't, quite. We've been through a lot of hell. It's not that. It's just that these three years I've been gone, I been remembering you and thinking about our little place. Can see it now. Guess the house'll need paint, and we'll have to do some fixin' on the barn. They'll look *about* the same, anyway

I remember the way the sun comes up
over the east ridge, and I can see the
oak tree over on the hill where we used
to go for our picnics. I haven't forgotten,
either, daughter Mary, that I promised
to take you for a picnic the day I got
home. We'll do that Sunday. I want
everything just like it was. So here's to
a sunny Sunday and a new start for all
of us!"

"Seems so unreal, Mother," says the girl.
"Dad comin' home. I've been waitin' so
long."

"I know, darlin'," says the mother.

"He wants everything just like it was!
Mother! We've just got to have that
picnic Sunday. Every letter he's written
he's mentioned it. Mother, it'd be terrible if it rained on Sunday!"

"We'd just have to postpone the picnic.
That's all."

"We couldn't do that! It wouldn't be the
same! It's just *got* to be nice weather!"

"Turn on the radio, dear. It's time for
the news. Maybe there'll be a weather
report."

"I'm almost afraid to," the girl says. But
she goes to the radio and snaps on the
button. Then she says, as the machine

**51**

WISCONSIN IS MY DOORSTEP

warms up: "Wonder if Daddy's changed? I can hardly remember how he looked. Isn't it funny, Mother? I remember we had a lot of picnics, and . . ."

"Hush," says Mother. "Here's the weather report."

Well, near as I can recall, here's what the weather experts *said* was gonna happen:

"High winds in Southern Wisconsin tonight and thunderstorms. For Central and Northern Wisconsin, increasing cloudiness tonight and thunderstorms Sunday."

"Oh, Mother," says the girl, and she begins to cry.

"It can't be helped, darlin'."

"But, Mother, he'd planned on it."

"Daddy'll understand. And maybe it won't rain!"

"It will. I know it will!"

So her mother went and put her arms around the girl and tried to comfort her. "You better go to bed now," she says finally. "I have a kind of feelin' it'll be a fine day tomorrow. But if it isn't, Daddy'll be so glad to get home, he won't notice at all!"

"But he will, Mother. He will!"

"You go to bed now, Mary."

"All right, Mother."

Well, the girl went to bed and after a while, I heard her sobbin' and sayin' over and over: "Please. Please! Just this once. Don't let it rain tomorrow. You can let it rain every other day all summer. But not tomorrow. Just this once!" And then she finally went to sleep.

Long about seven o'clock—or a little past—the next mornin' her mother called her. "Mary! Mary!"

"Yes, Mother?"

"Get up, dear. Daddy'll be comin' any minute!"

"Mother! You've let me sleep! Is it raining?"

"Look out and see."

"It's . . . Why, it's *clear!* The sun's shining! It's a beautiful day!"

"Just goes to show," says Mother, "that the weatherman *can* be wrong. Look! Isn't that a car? It is! Hurry, dear! We'll run out to the end of the lane! It's Dad!"

Yep. You can call it what you want to. Say it was chance, or explain it any way you please. Say it was that girl's prayers if you like. I'm not gonna tell you. I'm

53

just the old man with a long beard that sits up in the sky and pushes the clouds and the winds around. Well, I must be goin' now. You see, I have to keep the Wisconsin folks guessin'! But they don't seem to mind it too much! Wouldn't live any place else, I reckon.

Well, so long! I have a little storm to do up on the Baraboo Range this evenin'. Can't disappoint that young feller who was wishin' for me! He'll be drivin' up to Baraboo to see his gal tonight. Have a lot of fun with 'im! Bye!

# TRICKSTER ...

## *on my doorstep*

THERE'S humor aplenty to be found in any growing country, and the trick players furnish a lot of laughable yarns that the folks never grow tired of telling.

Wisconsin has, in her book of humorous memories, an especially famous prankster named Gene Shepard, from Rhinelander. Between the late 1880's and the middle 1920's Gene probably furnished Wisconsin with more laughs than any other one man. Gene was a crack timber cruiser—cruised a great deal of timber from Wisconsin to Western Canada and left the names of his friends, male and female, scattered throughout Northern Wisconsin, for he gave their names to numerous lakes and places. But what Gene enjoyed doing most was playing tricks; and here he comes now, a tall man with a black mustache.

"Howdy, Gene!"

"Howdy, fellow."

"What'd you do, Gene, to get so famous?"

"My goodness! What *didn't* I do?"

"How about telling us a few of your adventures?"

"Glad to oblige," says Gene. "Ever hear the adventure of the Kentucky Strong Man?"

"Can't say as I have."

" 'Twas mighty exciting. My friend, Matt Stapleton, was in on that one with me. Happened like this—"

We were waiting for a train one night at Gagen Junction. Couldn't catch the train for Rhinelander until two o'clock in the morning. We had considerable time to kill, so Matt said to me, "Gene, I'm cold."

"Me too."

"There's only one place in this berg open," said Matt. "That's the saloon. Do you suppose we could go in there and get warm, Gene?"

"Guess I could bear it," I said. "Come along."

And we walked to the saloon which was very full of lumberjacks celebratin' as they liked to do now and then.

"Quite a crowd in here," I said to Matt.

"Sure is. Ain't no room at the bar at all."

Then I noticed that there was quite a group of men bunched around one end of the bar. "What's the excitement over there?" I asked a feller standing next to me.

"Oh, it's that Kentucky man over there," he said. "See him? He's the big feller at the end of the bar. He's been raisin' the roof all evening. Listen to him!"

And then we could hear the Kentucky man all right. He was one of those settlers that had come into Wisconsin when Kentucky got too tame for 'em. "I'm the strongest jasper in all o' Kentuck!" he was roaring. "Yeah, an' I'm the strongest in all this here Wisconsin country too. I kin whup my weight in blood-fed wildcats! I'm a hard-drinkin', straight-shootin', hell-raisin', meat-fed, killin' man! I'm from ol' Kentuck, I am, an' I'm spoilin' fer a fight!"

"Aw, shut up," said the man next to him.

"Hey, whut's that?" bawled Kentuck.

"You ain't no killer."

"Oh, I ain't? Just looky here at my rifle. This here's a straight-shootin', shoulder-lovin' piece o' iron! Looky here at the stock. See them notches?"

"Yeah," said his neighbor. "I see them notches all right."

"Each one of them notches represents a man, son. Why, I just come from a feudin' down in ol' Kentuck. Picked off five McCoys, I did, one right after 'tother. See this here bowie knife? See them notches on the handle o' that knife? Y' see 'em? Let me tell you, brother, 'bout the first sixty

57

or seventy pore critters that was crazy enough to cross knives with me. Why, I mind me the time a little guy, six foot ten tall he was, come after me . . . an' . . ."

Yes, that Kentuck man was really carryin' on. Matt and me was scared. We was both about ready to get out of there when I got a good glimpse of the rifle the Kentuck was carryin'. "That's a fine rifle he's got, Matt."

"Yeah," said Matt. "And he can use it too. He's a killer, all right."

"Maybe," I said. Then I got a glimpse of the Kentuck's knife. "That's a gold-handled bowie knife he's got there, too, Matt. I'd sure like to have that rifle and that knife."

"Don't you start nothin' with that Kentuck man, Gene," said Matt. "He'd carve you like a turkey."

"You scared of him, Matt?" I asked.

"Yeah, I'm scared. Let's go."

"Wait," I said. "I got an idea."

"Oh Lordy!" said Matt.

"Here's what we're gonna do, Matt . . ."

"Listen to him," said Matt.

"I'm a ring-tailed, rip-snortin', fire-eatin', hell-kitty! Who wants to fight? Huh? Speak up! I'll fight any sixteen-eighteen men here. All to once! Come on! Who'll be first?"

"Let's go," said Matt.

"Here's what we're gonna do," I repeated. "In a little while you're gonna fall down, Matt, and pretend like you're havin' a fit."

"Me?"

"Yeah. Then . . ."

"No, Gene, no!" said Matt, makin' his way to the door. "That Kentuck will cut my heart out."

"No, he won't. I guarantee it."

"By God, just listen to him!" said Matt. And I will admit that listenin' to that Kentuck was makin' shivers dance along my own spine! He was a talker!

"I'm a cold-blooded killer," he was yellin'. "Look at them scars on my chest! Them's knife scars, boys! Why, I been in a thousand knife fights! Yeah, an' killed my man every time! I'm the sole survivor o' m' clan, I am! Killed seventy-five men, I did! Who wants to fight? Huh? Speak up! I'll fight any twenty-five men in this here saloon. Yeah, and give you the underholts, too! Come on! Come on!"

"Ain't you scared, Gene?" said Matt.

"We're gonna tame that Kentuck wild man, Matt. You 'n me."

"You do it, Gene," Matt said. "I'm feelin' kind of sick. Think I'll go outside a minute."

"You can't, Matt," I said holding him. "Now listen. In a little while you fall down on the floor and begin to holler and scream."

"I can't do it, Gene."

"Drink this," I said, getting him a tumbler of *Ol' Tanglefoot* from the bar. "Drink this an' you'll feel better."

"I need somethin'," said Matt and downed it.

"You feel better?"

"Why . . . Yeah," said Matt. "Yeah, I do."

"Can you throw that fit now?"

**59**

"Why, certainly. Say, Gene, who was that was yellin' for a fight? Gene! What'm I sayin'?"

"*Ol' Tanglefoot*'s great stuff, Matt. All right. You ready?"

"I guess so," said Matt.

"Then start throwin' your fit!" And such a fit you never seen before. Matt hollered wild, piercin' hollers you coulda heard for nine-ten mile. He got down on the floor of that saloon. He rolled. He kicked. He gave out strange laughs. He yelled he was gonna kill everybody in the saloon.

"He's havin' a fit," I shouted. "I want the strongest man here to help me hold him! Quick! Who's the strongest man here? Well, speak up! Ain't there no strong men here?"

"That there Kentuck man claims to be strong, mister," said a fellow.

"You Kentucky man," I yelled. "You ain't afraid o' nothin'. Come here and help me."

"I ain't so strong, mister," said Kentuck backing away.

"Yes, you are," I said, getting him by the arm. "Don't be modest. Come over here. My friend needs help."

"We-ell, all right."

"But be careful," I said. "My friend's liable to be dangerous. Now! Grab aholt of him!"

And quite a bit against his judgment, the Kentuck grabbed Matt on one side, and I grabbed him on the other. We was tryin' our best to hold him down, when Kentuck said to me, "What's wrong with him, mister?"

60

"He was bitten by a mad dog last month," I grunted. "I reckon he's got rabies."

"Huh?" yelled Kentuck. "Hey! He's bit me! Bit me on the leg!"

"Aw," I said sadly, "that's too bad. Say, *you'll* get rabies now."

"Me?" cries Kentuck. "*I'll* get rabies? Save me! I'm gonna die!"

"I'll save you, Kentuck," I shouted. "Quick, somebody! Give me a bucket of water!"

"There's a bucket behind the bar," yelled the bartender.

"Give it to me. Thanks!" And I heaved the bucket of cold water over the Kentucky man's head. "That water'll help cool your blood, Kentuck."

"I'm pretty nigh drowned," says Kentuck. "Now what'll I do?"

"You gotta *run!*" I said. "That's the only cure for the rabies. Run and don't stop runnin'. Leave your knife an' gun here so's you can run faster. You hear?"

"I hear you," said Kentuck. "Lemme out!"

"Open the door for him," I said, and out run Kentuck into the night, headin' south. Maybe back to Kentucky.

"All right, Matt," I continued, "you can get up off the floor now. And since that Kentuck man won't be back for 'em, I might as well take that rifle and that knife. Well, time for our train. So long, boys!"

"Seems like, Gene," I say, as Gene finishes the story of the Kentucky Strong Man, "that I've heard you created

61

considerable of a mystery up at Rhinelander, Wisconsin, one time. Something about a strange animal you found out in the woods."

"Oh that," replies Gene, "that happened back about 1900. The scene is the Oneida County Fair at Rhinelander. There's considerable excitement about what's in a certain booth at the Fair. A booth erected by myself. In fact, I'm sittin' right out in front of that booth now, talkin' to my friend, Matt Stapleton. . . ."

MATT:   Come on now, Gene, what you got in this booth?

GENE:   Matt, I got something in this booth that'll make history; that'll make Wisconsin the most famous state in the Union.

MATT:   Yeah. But what is it?

GENE:   You'll see, by and by. Well, well! Here comes the Mayor! Howdy, Mr. Mayor!

MAYOR:  Gene, this trick playin' o' yours has got to stop! Man you're givin' Rhinelander a bad name.

GENE:   Why, what'd you mean, Mayor?

MAYOR:  Well, I got a complaint agin you. Some lady come to me awhile ago and told me you'd claimed to have found a wonderful perfumed moss growin' out in the forest. Said you'd led her around the woods for three days, finally showed her the moss. Said it smelt right nice, too. Said she took some of that moss down to Madison and come to find out, you'd put drugstore perfume on it. She was right mad!

GENE: Aw now, Mayor ...

MAYOR: And looky here! Just looky what a feller brought to my office this mornin'!

GENE: Why, you got my rubber Muskellunge there, Mayor. Where'd you get it?

MAYOR: Feller who's been stayin' up to your camp at Ballard Lake brought it in. Said the fishin' had been poor, and everybody was about to pack up and go home when they seen a big Muskie breakin' water and cavortin' around. Said they all went back fishin' and fished a week longer without any luck. Then, by cracky, they found this here *rubber fish* was what they seen! Feller was right wrought up! Gene, you got to cut it out!

GENE: Here, have a cigar, Mayor.

MAYOR: One of them *explodin'* cigars of yours? No sir! And look here. *What you got in this here exhibit tent?*

GENE: It's a secret, Mayor.

MAYOR: Well, I ain't gonna have you ... Here comes a newspaper reporter!

REPORTER: Mr. Shepard! You are Mr. Shepard, aren't you?

63

GENE: Why, sure I am. Who're you?

REPORTER: I'm Harry Wilson. I'm a reporter from the *Milwaukee Journal*. My editor got a wire sayin' you had a wonderful new discovery . . . somethin' that'd revolutionize civilization. He sent me right up to Rhinelander to see about it.

GENE: Well, well! Mayor, we're gettin' famous.

MAYOR: Now, see here, Gene . . .

REPORTER: What *is* this discovery, Mr. Shepard?

GENE: Son, no mortal eyes but mine have ever looked on this here discovery.

(*A Teacher appears.*)

TEACHER: Where's Gene Shepard? Oh, here you are!

GENE: Why, if it ain't Miss Lucy Moore. Howdy, Miss Lucy! This here young feller is Harry Wilson from Milwaukee. Newspaper man. Harry, meet Miss Lucy Moore, our teacher around here.

REPORTER: Morning, Miss Moore.

TEACHER: Gene Shepard, you're corrupting the children in the school! All they can talk about is your pranks! How can I teach them to respect the *truth* when you teach 'em that it's more fun to fool people than it is to learn the *truth!*

MAYOR: That's right, Miss Lucy.

TEACHER: Mr. Mayor, I insist that you make Gene Shepard take whatever it is he's got in this tent and throw it in the lake!

MAYOR:     I agree, Gene...

REPORTER:  Now, hold on, folks. I came clear up here
           from Milwaukee to get a story and I'm gonna
           get it! Mr. Shepard, what *do* you have in that
           tent?

GENE:      Why, I got a *Hodag* in here.

REPORTER:  What?

MAYOR:     Huh?

TEACHER:   You have a *fake* in there!

REPORTER:  What was that name again?

TEACHER:   Fake!

GENE:      Hodag. H-O-D-A-G!

REPORTER:  What in tarnation is a Hodag?

MAYOR:     Gene, if this here's another prank...

GENE:      Honest, Mayor, I got a real Hodag. Only one
           in captivity!

TEACHER:   Are you going to take *his* word for it, young
           man?

REPORTER:  Let's see it, Mr. Shepard.

GENE:      After while. First I got to tell you how I cap-
           tured him.

REPORTER:  Go ahead. I'm ready to take down every word.

GENE:      Well, you know how it goes in the lumber
           camps: always a lot of different kinds of fel-
           lers around, and all of 'em masters of strong
           language. And you know that the critter that
           gets cussed most and longest is the ox. Ain't
           that so, Matt?

MATT:      Shore is. Shore is. I remember...

**65**

GENE:    Well, I'd been doin' some deep readin' lately, and had figured out that all those cusses flung down on the poor camp ox had to come to roost! You know, the hide of an ox is pretty tough, but you keep cussin' him long enough, you're bound to make an impression. It's true, ain't it, that a constant drippin' of water 'll wear away stone?

MATT:    That's sure true, Gene.

GENE:    Now you know that in the lumber camps it's customary to cremate an ox when he dies.

MATT:    That's so, Gene. I mind the time ...

GENE:    And I got it figured out that it takes seven years of constant burnin' to dislodge all those cusses from the body of that ox!

TEACHER: Hokum! Pure hokum!

GENE:    Now, Miss Lucy, it ain't p'lite to interrupt. Let me finish. Well, there was one ox, and even Paul Bunyan used to tell about this, that was cussed so much and so often, that he must have had a million devils inside him. The fellers at that particular camp, when that ox came to die, knew they'd have to burn that critter for seven long years—just to get peace for his soul. So they did.

TEACHER: Hokum! Pure hokum!

GENE:    And at the end of that seven years, you know what happened?

REPORTER: This is interesting, Mr. Shepard! My editor'll

love it. What happened at the end of seven years?

GENE: Well, sir, as the fire slowly died down at the end of that seven years, a mystical animal rose from the ashes!

REPORTER: You mean . . . that animal was the . . . Hodag?

GENE: Sure!

TEACHER: Hokum!

MAYOR: Nonsense, Gene! Nonsense!

TEACHER: Fake!

GENE: So, one day last week I was takin' a little quiet stroll out 'n the woods, when my nostrils were suddenly assailed by a terrible odor. I sniffed, and then I heard a long, terrible growl!

MAYOR: You heard a . . . what?

TEACHER: Hokum! Pure hokum!

GENE: Looking farther in the underbrush I saw a horrible sight: a critter such as mortal eyes had never before set upon!

REPORTER: What'd it look like?

GENE: It was something like a dinosaur in the back; its tail had a spearlike end. Sharp spines, a foot and a half apart, ran down its spine. It had thick claws, part hooves too, sort of like an ox. The head had two sharp horns. It was snortin' and breathin' fire. Well, I got out of there fast, came home and studied out what it was!

TEACHER: Hokum!

GENE: I figured out what I was gonna do! Now you folks know, I'm a pretty brave man. Why, if I was to fight a bear, I'd toss my gun into the brush, throw away my bowie knife, and give that bear both underholts, just to have a fair tussle! Ain't that so, Matt?

MATT: Well, now Gene ...

GENE: So I figured out how to catch that Hodag critter. Now, I knowed from my readin' that the Hodag wouldn't eat anything but white bulldogs, and then only on Sunday, so I hit on the scheme of diggin' a big pit—you know, like they catch elephants in ... ?

TEACHER: Like they catch suckers in!

GENE: And I got me a pair of white bulldogs and went out there in the woods. Well, I found that critter snortin' around and mighty hungry of a Sunday mornin', and by careful maneuverin' of those dogs, I was able to get the terrible Hodag into that pit! Oh, it was a horrifyin' sight. The Hodag tore up whole trees as he came. And man, he came fast! Just as he was about to clamp his great jaws on me he disappeared into the pit!

MAYOR: Now, Gene, that's just a bit tall ...

GENE: And I got the Hodag right here in this tent, boys! Step right up, everybody, and see the terrible Hodag! Don't be afraid! Only twenty-five cents to see the marvel!

TEACHER: Mr. Mayor, if you allow Gene Shepard ...

REPORTER: What a story! My editor will *love* it!

(*A Professor appears*)

PROFESSOR: How-de-do, folks. I'm Professor Jones from the University. Got a wire from Gene Shepard saying he had an unusual, prehistoric specimen. Is Gene Shepard here?

GENE: I'm Gene Shepard. Howdy, Professor. You come up to see the Hodag?

PROFESSOR: Why, I presume so. Is the ... specimen in this tent?

GENE: Sure. I'm gonna open it up just as soon as I get a crowd! Step up! See the wonderful Hodag! Only twenty-five cents! Right this way for the most stupendous sight ever seen by modern man. Come a little closer, folks!

TEACHER: Mayor, I demand that you close this shameful exhibition. Where does *truth* stand, Mayor, in the face of this disgraceful sham?

MAYOR: Why, I don't rightly know, Miss Lucy.

TEACHER: Then make Gene Shepard go home!

MAYOR: Gene, I reckon ...

GENE: Folks, they're trying to stop you from viewing this amazing spectacle! Do you all want to see the Hodag?

CROWD: Sure! Let us in. Where's the Hodag? Here's *my* money. Open up, Gene!

TEACHER: Professor Jones! Surely you won't permit this horrible farce!

PROFESSOR: Why, I'm just a spectator, ma'am...

MAYOR: Gene, let Professor Jones go in and inspect this critter of yours. If he says it's all right, why... Would that be satisfactory, Miss Lucy?

TEACHER: Certainly. If the Professor says it's all right...

PROFESSOR: Shall I go in, Mr. Shepard?

GENE: Why, certainly. Come right in, Professor. (*They go in.*)

PROFESSOR: Humm. It's dark in the tent. What's this all about, Gene? I got your wire and I hurried up here fast as I...What's *that* thing?

GENE: It's the Hodag, Professor.

PROFESSOR: Uncanny! Marvelous!

GENE: Marvelous, uncanny! That's right, Professor.

PROFESSOR: The most marvelous *hoax* of the century.

GENE: Hoax, Professor?

PROFESSOR: Naturally. But a fine job of wood carving, Gene. What's the idea?

GENE: Professor, us folks need somethin' unusual in our lives. We need legends. Ain't that so? Why'd we make up all those Paul Bunyan stories? 'Cause we like unusual things! We like to be fooled! We like fun. We like to laugh. Why, we'll remember this Hodag for years and years! Professor, you ain't gonna give me away?

PROFESSOR: Gene, when you put it like that, I'm not going

to give you away. Go out there and let 'em in!
And I'm going to stay and watch the fun!

GENE: Thanks, Professor. I like a man with a sense of humor.

(*They go back outside.*)

MAYOR: Professor, what about it? What's Gene got in there?

PROFESSOR: Mr. Mayor, he's got the most amazing, marvelous . . .

MAYOR: He has? You mean . . .

PROFESSOR: People will remember the Hodag for a hundred years. They will flock to Rhinelander! Rhinelander will be known as the "Hodag City."

MAYOR: It will?

TEACHER: Mayor! What're you doing?

MAYOR: I'm going to bark for this exhibit myself! Step right up! Step right up, everybody! See the Hodag! The amazing, wonderful Hodag! The sight of the century! See the Hodag and tell your friends. Tell 'em Rhinelander'll be the "Hodag City"! Step right up!

PROFESSOR: Gene, the Mayor's taken over your show!

REPORTER: What a story for the *Milwaukee Journal!* Gee! Can we go in now, Mr. Shepard?

GENE: Sure. Just wait'll I give the Mayor a cigar. Here, Mayor, have a cigar!

MAYOR: Thanks, Gene. Thanks.

GENE: Here. I'll light it for you.

MAYOR: Thanks, Gene. Thanks. Say, I was wrong, Gene. Forgive me! You'll put Rhinelander on the map! All right, folks! Go right in!
(*There is the sound of a loud explosion.*)

GENE: That explosion was the Mayor's cigar blowing up. But don't let it bother you. Everybody's having a wonderful time viewing the greatest hoax Wisconsin ever had: the Hodag!

# MIRACLE ...

## on my doorstep

EVERYWHERE in the Belgian settlement on the Green Bay Peninsula, the people were dying of Asiatic cholera. Strong men—apparently well at night—would be found dead in the morning, the skin on their faces turned black, their eyes sunken into the sockets. It seemed that newcoming pioneers had brought destruction to the new country. There was great sorrow.

The people stopped coming from Belgium. The Wisconsin pioneers were left alone, and from one sorrow they went to another, for food, after a time, there was none.

The men sought work in the faraway cities, walking the whole way to Milwaukee. The women were left alone in the wilderness, lonely and afraid.

In the Brice family cabin, Mamma Brice was very much afraid when the wolves howled at night. "Oh, the wolves," she would murmur, "always the wolves! Why did we leave Belgium? Why did we leave *home?*"

But in the Brice household there was the daughter, Adele, a girl of eighteen; a simple Belgian girl who had faith.

"Do not fear, Mother," she would reply. "The wolves will not hurt us. God is with us."

"We do not even have a church. Only at Bay Settlement, ten miles away, is there a church. Why did we leave home!"

But Adele only said, "Some day we will have a church, Mamma."

There were other sorrows to come. In 1857 came a financial crisis that stopped the work in the cities. The men had nothing then. They came trudging home, worn out, discouraged. When Papa Brice came home, Mamma could only ask, "What will we do now, Papa?"

"We have plenty of timber," replied Papa. "But we have no oxen, no horses. We cannot move the timber out. In Green Bay they said pine shingles might bring a dollar and a half per thousand. If we cannot move the logs, we can at least make the shingles!"

Oh, there were hard times! Young and old, they became shingle makers, those Belgians. Father and mother

74

sawed the trees into eighteen-inch bolts. The children split them. Father shaved them down and bound them into bundles of shingles.

The lake shore was miles away. Still, the bundles were carried there by hand. And a day's wage was so very little, but the families were kept alive. Their needs were few. Gunny sacks there were for clothing, and wooden sabots were used in place of leather shoes. Bread was a problem that was worrisome to Mamma Brice.

"Bread, Papa," she would say. "We must have bread."

It was indeed a problem. Wheat was sown among the forest trees and cut and threshed by hand. But there were no mills near by to grind it. So Mamma Brice would continue, "I must take wheat to the mill."

They were accustomed to heavy work, those Belgian women. The wheat, so carefully grown, was put in a bag. The bag was then tied at the open end, and the other end was made into a hood which Mamma put over her head. The bag on her back then, she trudged all day through the forest, her feet bare, and her wooden shoes dangling from a cord about her neck; for the shoes must be clean when she made her appearance at the mill. Ten, fifteen miles away was the mill, and when she returned there was flour, but there was also great weariness. "Papa," she would say, "I am so tired, so very, very tired. Papa, has God forsaken his people?"

"Sometimes it seems so, Mamma."

Mamma sighed. "If we only had a church near by where we might worship!"

"The Belgian settlers are talking, Mamma. They're saying, 'Let us return to Belgium.' Mamma, shall we leave Wisconsin?"

"It seems that God has forsaken us," said Mamma sadly. "I will return if you wish."

"Here we have land," Papa said. "In land we are rich as the landed gentry in Belgium. But in everything else we are poor. I am ready to return, Mamma."

But in that household there was also the girl Adele.

"Mamma, Papa, do not give up," she pleaded. "Stay! God has *not* forsaken you."

"And why has He not?" said Mamma. "There has been no sign. There has been only starvation, sorrow, weariness."

"What could *you* know of the ways of God?" Papa said to Adele. "You, a girl!"

"Even the priest at Bay Settlement is discouraged," said Mamma.

But Adele only said simply, "I do know, Mamma. Have I ever feared the forests? Have I feared the wild beasts? When I walk alone in the forest, the trees whisper to me. Always they whisper that God is near. Mamma, Papa, it is very wrong to doubt God."

"You are a good girl, Adele," Papa answered wearily. "But your dreams are not enough."

"Let me go to Bay Settlement tomorrow, Papa. Let me go there and pray for all of us. Please, Papa."

"But Bay Settlement is a long way. Ten miles through the forest."

76

"Let me go. Please let me go, Papa."

"It can do no harm," Mamma said. "Let her go. Her prayers may bring us luck."

"My prayers will be answered," said Adele. "I know they'll be answered."

"Go if you like, then," said Papa. "But start early and return before nightfall."

"Yes, Papa."

So on the morrow this young girl set out for the Settlement. And for what follows I must ask you to believe, as I believe; for there was only goodness in the heart of this child.

As she walked the trees whispered to her, the birds sang; indeed, as she walked near them, they seemed to be singing for her alone. The sunlight filtering through the leaves made strange patterns on the ground. The streams tinkled in their beds—of such things are visions made, perhaps. But certainly in the being of this young girl there was no thought of vision. There was humility and prayer, the forest was close and friendly about her, and indeed God seemed very near; yet of Heavenly symbol there was nothing. The forest was to her as always, and the fingers of the wind touched only as usual; still, as Adele climbed a little knoll, exactly there in the space between the trunks of two white birch trees, appeared a blinding white light. Surely such a light as one had never dreamed before. And as Adele cowered breathlessly before it, her lips moving in soundless prayers, her ears were hearing unworldly music.

When she dared at last to raise her eyes to the light, it

had changed. Indeed, it had taken a definite form; and between the two trees, there in the lonely forest, stood a marvelously beautiful lady clothed in dazzlingly white garments. Her eyes were deep and dark, and she smiled radiantly and kindly upon the girl who now knelt before her. Adele only whispered, "Oh . . . oh . . . oh."

It had happened before. Joan of Arc saw visions and rose to be a leader of her people. The early French settlers in the valley of the St. Lawrence were comforted by a report that the Virgin had appeared in a vision among them. Here, in the Wisconsin wilderness, a simple Belgian girl had seen a vision of the Holy Mother. Would she, too, be the instrument through which her people might regain faith and courage?

These things were not in Adele's mind as she hurried on to the church which Father Daems had built at the Bay Settlement. She was only a frightened child seeking explanation for what she had seen. At the church, trembling, she told of her experience to the priest.

"My child," said the priest, "are you certain you saw what you describe?"

"I did, Father. I did. You must believe me!"

"I believe you, Adele," replied the priest.

"What shall I do, Father?"

"You must have courage, Adele," said Father Daems. "If ever the vision appears before you again, you must say, 'In the name of our Lord, who are you and what do you wish of me?' Do you understand, Adele?"

78

"I understand, Father. But to speak to the Virgin . . . Father, I couldn't."

"If the Virgin appeared to you, Adele," said the priest kindly, "it was for some very great reason. Do not be afraid then. Rather give thanks that you, a poor settler's daughter, should be the subject of this visitation. Will you do this?"

"Yes, Father," whispered the girl. "But *I'm afraid!*"

So Adele turned back home, and as she walked the forest seemed to become still. There was no wind in the trees. No birds sang. The streams were hushed. Adele knew only her trembling heart pounding harder and harder as she neared the little knoll with the two white birch trees standing still and straight. As she climbed the knoll her knees became weaker and weaker, so that before the two trees she sank to her knees. And slowly as Adele raised her eyes, the vision was there again before her—the beautiful lady in white, the same smile.

"Who are you?" whispered the girl. "In the name of our Lord, who are you and what do you want of me?"

"I am the Queen of Heaven," said the beautiful lady, "who prays for the conversion of sinners. Do you the same; for through you will come the salvation of your people. Through you the instruction of the children. Through you the faith of your people will grow strong again."

The vision faded away, and Adele ran home with the news. The story spread through all the Belgian settlements.

Of course, not everyone believed. Adele's parents believed; for they knew Adele, and they knew she could not lie. But there were others.

"She had a dream," said one neighbor. "She was always a dreamer, that Adele."

"Always walking alone," said another. "Always talking with the birds and the animals! What might not such a one imagine?"

But there were others, perhaps the ones most lacking in faith, who saw here an answer to their prayers. A sign. Indeed, most of the settlers believed in the miracle, and the simple girl became a great teacher.

She went from home to home, from neighborhood to neighborhood, restoring the faith of the parents and instructing the children. The people accepted the story.

And this belief became dominant. From far and near, from Green Bay and the distant cabins in Union, Brussels, and Gardner in Door County came people to look upon the holy ground where Adele saw the Virgin. And that same fall, the settlers built a chapel on the very spot, and a schoolhouse close by. Young and old the settlers regained their faith, and as they regained their faith in God and the new country to which they had come, their condition began to improve.

Still, those highest in her church did not believe Adele's story. The bishop did not believe.

"It's a myth!" he roared. "An imposition! Adele Brice is an ignorant girl with a sensational story!"

And as Adele continued to affirm the truth of her story,

she was denied the Holy Sacrament and was treated as an outcast from the Church.

But this made no difference to the Belgian folk. They did not waver in their faith, but gathered in large numbers to worship at the "Chapel of the Holy Virgin." And August 15, the day of Adele's vision, was regarded as a Holy Day. And on August 15 many pilgrims from distant states and cities came here to pray. Yes, cripples came too, and with triumphant faith were able to walk out whole, leaving their crutches behind.

And finally there happened a great event which forced the Church to recognize the mighty faith of Adele Brice— Sister Adele.

It was October 1871. There had been great changes in the lives of those Belgian settlers. How Papa Brice loved to tell of his good fortune!

"Mamma," he would say, "we are as rich as Belgian gentlemen! We have a sawmill and a gristmill. We have cows, Mamma. Are you not glad we did not return to Belgium as you wanted?"

"It was more you than I who wanted to go," Mamma would reply.

"Oh, you forget so easily."

"I do not forget that our strength is in God. I do not forget that, Papa."

"No," answered Papa, "we do not forget. Never again. There is but one worry now. The forest is so dry this fall. So very, very dry."

And no rains fell. As time went on the nervous settlers could see at nightfall flashes of red flame far away, and the whole skies were deadened by smoke. And then suddenly the terrible tragedy struck. It happened on Sunday, October 8, 1871. Folks afterwards called it "Saddy" October 8; for it was the saddest day the Belgians ever knew.

In the morning the day was quite ordinary. There was some smoke in the air. In the afternoon the wind came up fresh and strong. In the evening the air was very still. Then, out of nowhere, came a great gust of wind followed by a great roaring. Then the flames shot up and up. Great trees came crashing down. Birds screamed and wild animals bounded into the clearings, mad with fear. Out of the sky came a whirlwind, a tornado of flame, falling in great clouds out of the sky; falling on the homes of the people; falling upon them, destroying everything. Everything. Only one thought was in the minds of the people: "It is the end," they shrieked. "The end of the world!"

Oh, there were many tales of sorrow. At Williamsville, ten miles south of Sturgeon Bay, sixty settlers were burned to death as they huddled together in the middle of a three-acre field. "Holy Mary, Mother of God, pray for us!" they cried. "Pray for us. Help us!" And so they called and prayed until the terrible flame crashed down upon them.

Everywhere there was terror. Homes, barns, granaries filled with the fruits of a summer's toil were utterly destroyed. The cattle, so newly purchased and so prized by these agricultural folk, were burned to crisp while fleeing

82

through the woods. The plow handles were burned in the furrow; the logs in the corduroy roads were consumed.

There was much wonder about Sister Adele. Sister Adele, with her little church and school there on the spot where she once saw the Virgin; for certainly these buildings were in the very path of the raging flames. And truly enough, the good sisters who had come to help Sister Adele with her sacred work were huddled about her as they watched the great flames creep nearer and nearer.

"Sister Adele," said one, "should we not go now before it's too late?"

"Should we not, Sister," pleaded another. "Let us go. Please, Sister Adele."

"We are the servants of the will of God," replied Sister Adele. "We will stay. This is holy ground."

"The air is so hot and heavy. We can hardly breathe."

"Have courage. God is with us. Come, I will lead you in song so that God may know we are not afraid. Sing! Sing, Sisters!"

And as they sang, one of the sisters gave a great cry.

"The flames! The flames! The flames are upon us!"

"They will not touch this church," said Adele quietly. "Let us finish the hymn."

It is true that when the mighty flames reached the tiny wilderness chapel, they divided, passing on either side of the chapel and school; neither was burned, and none of the Sisters of Adele was the least bit injured.

When the bishop heard this he was no longer able to withhold his blessing.

"I believe that Sister Adele's vision was true," he stated. "I hereby restore her and her following to the Holy Sacrament."

And though the people suffered, and hundreds died in the fire, they had learned their lesson. No more did they cry to return to the Old Country. The fire was the will of God; and was not the sparing of the chapel witness that God was with them still? The ways of God are wonderful and strange. Not theirs to question. They would submit, but they would never again lose faith. Homes could be rebuilt, new mills erected. They would get more cows. The main thing was courage. Yes, and thankfulness for the freedom of the new land. It would take work, but what Belgian is afraid of work?

And so it was. Through the following years the Belgians worked and prospered. And among them, so long as she lived, was Sister Adele, the girl who saw one morning the vision of the Holy Mother appearing between two tall white birch trees; * who through her vision restored the faith of the Belgian folk in the Wisconsin wilderness.

* Sister Adele's Chapel may be seen near Robinsonville, Wisconsin.

# HOSS THIEVES ...

## on my doorstep

I T'S a funny thing about
the Finch family—*The Fightin' Finches*,* they were called.
They were supposed to be mighty tough, rough folks, the
leadin' outlaw family probably in Wisconsin's history.
Yet some facts don't jibe with the yarns. One of the best
known Finches was Ben. Benomi was his real name. He is
known in folktale as a great hoss thief and a mighty slick
expert with his shootin' irons. Yet at the town of White-

* For these yarns I am chiefly indebted to a mimeographed publication:
*The Fighting Finches*, Federal Writer's Project, Folklore Section, Madison,
Wisconsin, 1937.

water, Wisconsin, the records show that a Benomi Finch. who I am told was one and the same with the famous outlaw, was captain of the local militia in the Black Hawk War; that he was apparently a civic leader and a public benefactor. How come?

Well, there are just three explanations. One, the tales have made Benomi out to be something he wasn't; two, he was a mighty slick operator and insinuated himself into the bosom of Whitewater society; or three, the Whitewater folks were in cahoots with a gang of outlaws. Take your pick.

At any rate the Finches had a hide-out, which to this day is known as Hide-Out Swamp, from which they rode forth to steal fine horses in the surrounding Jefferson, Rock, and Walworth counties.

Although there are no records which show that the Finches actually committed a murder, there are many tales about their love of fighting. It appears that they departed from St. Joseph, Michigan, seeking combat, since they arrived in the Wisconsin country at approximately the time of the Black Hawk War: 1832. It also appears that the St. Joseph citizens were delighted to see the family go. Nobody wished them any hard luck, but all were glad to be rid of their belligerent ways.

The yarns about the Finches are many, and here on my doorstep are a whole bunch of people from Southeastern Wisconsin, present and past residents, who've come to tell some of the best ones. Here's a fellow who's made up a song about the famous outlaws . . .

BALLAD SINGER: The Finches were bold,
      The Finches were mad.
      Their women were beautiful,
      The men were bad.
      But one thing certain you must agree,
      The Finches were the worst in the whole
        countree!

"I am aware that they were a bad outfit," I reply, "but just what did they *do*, anyway?"

"Hold on, friend," says a farmer, "listen to my neighbor sing."

BALLAD SINGER: Of sturdy pioneers
      One hears so much,
      Honest, hard-working
      Thrifty and such.
      But sometimes a man who was hardly a
        saint,
      Would rustle fine hosses then disguise
        'em with paint!

"I can explain *that*," says an old fellow stepping forward. "My name's Tom Jordan. I'm a Wisconsin pioneer. Year 1832. Came out here to Southern Wisconsin from New York State to break me some new land and set up my family.

"Say, this Southern Wisconsin country's the place for me! Deep soil, lots of game. Passenger pigeons so thick in the sky, ya can't see the sun sometimes.

"When I come here I had me a fine team o' hosses—Jeff and Turk. Good workers. Turk was the best hoss, a beauty. Had a white streak straight down his face. Well, went out to my lean-to barn one mornin', and Turk was gone. No sign of 'im any place."

"What'd you do then, Tom?" I ask.

"When I couldn't find Turk anywhere," Tom replies, "I sent the word all around the countryside: My hoss Turk, Lost, Strayed, *or Stolen!*"

"Must've left you in a tight fix, no hosses."

"Sure did. And Spring was comin' on. One mornin' my wife said to me . . ."

| | |
|---|---|
| WIFE: | Tom, I heard from the neighbors acrost the valley that there was a horse dealer in Lake Mills offerin' up some good horses for sale. |
| PIONEER: | That so? Well, maybe I better get to town. We got to have another hoss! Guess I'll be on my way. 'Bye! |
| WIFE: | 'Bye, Tom. |
| PIONEER: | So I went into the village, and there in a big barn were these traders with their hosses. Say, did they have some fine ones! We'd never seen hosses like 'em anywhere. |
| FARMER: | See any hoss you liked particularly well, Tom? |

PIONEER: Yes. A big bay, just the size and shape of my missin' hoss, Turk! I took a shine to that one right away. Said to the trader, "This 's a fine hoss, mister. Just like one I lost a while back, except my hoss Turk had a white strip down his face. This hoss ain't got a white strip."

TRADER: No, he ain't, son.

PIONEER: But I'll buy this one anyhow.

TRADER: All right, son. It'll cost you two hundred dollars!

PIONEER: Two hundred! Say, that's high!

TRADER: Hosses come high, son.

PIONEER: Well, all right. Takes my last cent, but here's your money.

TRADER: Thanks, son. Thanks. You're gonna git used to that hoss in no time, son. No time at all!

PIONEER: And you know, when I led that new hoss home, he seemed to act like he knew the road. Never had to guide a bit. Turned right into my gate he did by himself.

He was a good worker, and with Spring comin' on he began real soon losin' his winter hair. One mornin' my wife said:

WIFE: Tom! Look out there! There's Turk grazin' out by the woodpile! It's our missin' Turk! He's come home!

89

PIONEER:     We run out there, and do ya know what? It was Turk all right, sure. But it was that *new hoss,* too. Those rascals had painted old Turk's face, and now the painted hair'd rubbed off. *I'd bought my own hoss!*

FARMER:      The Finches were bad! They'd skin you every time!

"Didn't anybody ever catch those Finches?" I ask as the Pioneer finishes his story.

"Some *say* they caught several," replies the farmer, "but to tell you the truth only *one* Finch was caught, and he was the wrong one at that. You see, 'twas like this: Henry Dodge was Governor of the new Wisconsin Territory. Madison was the new capital, and the year was 1838. Seems there was a settler, a Norwegian . . . :

BALLAD SINGER: One day a Norwegian
              Came astaggerin' in.
              Says he: Them Finches
              Are full o' sin;
              Beat me up an' chased me off my ground;
              When I tried to get even, they run me
                  clear to town!

FARMER:      First thing that Norwegian did was to bust into Governor Henry Dodge's office. The Governor took a look at him and yelled:—

GOVERNOR:    What's the matter with you, sir? Look

like you been cut and hacked by a band of red skins, sir! State your business. I'm the Governor o' this Territory, and I'm mighty busy. Mighty busy. Incidentally, I can whip any man in Wisconsin. State your business!

NORWEGIAN: Mr. Governor, they beat me up! Chased me clear to Madison from Lake Koshkonong!

GOVERNOR: Who beat you up, sir? Nobody can beat up a citizen o' Wisconsin! Wisconsin people are the greatest fighters on earth!

NORWEGIAN: The Finches beat me up! I was out pulling stumps on my place when a dozen of 'em grabbed me.

GOVERNOR: Twelve to one! They can't do it! We play fair in Wisconsin!

NORWEGIAN: They said there wasn't room in Koshkonong Township for anybody but Finches.

GOVERNOR: They did? We'll see about that, sir. Just wait'll I call the Sheriff! Sheriff Bird! Come in here, sir!

SHERIFF: What's the matter, Governor?

GOVERNOR: Want you to go down to Koshkonong! Bring back one of them Finches!

NORWEGIAN: I don't know, Mr. Governor. They're mighty mean folks! Doubt if you catch one of 'em.

**91**

GOVERNOR: Sheriff, exhaust the power of the county, sir! And if that don't work, I'll call out the militia, by gad, sir! If that Finch tribe is going to run this Wisconsin Territory, I'll mighty soon find it out, sir!

SHERIFF: I'll go, Governor.

GOVERNOR: And bring back a Finch, or don't come back!

SHERIFF: All right, Governor!

BALLAD SINGER: Sheriff rode away
Just as skeered as could be;
For the Finches were lords
O' the whole countree.

An' he figured hard as he loaded his gun,
That ketchin' a Finch
Wouldn't be much fun!

SHERIFF: Yes, mister, I was skeered! Them Finches was the fastest and straightest shooters in all o' Wisconsin. I didn't know what to do. Well, I stole up clost to the Finch house. 'Twas right early in the mornin' and didn't seem to be anybody up yet. But I heard the sound o' wood bein' chopped out in the back yard. I took a good look, and I seen it was a Finch!

FARMER: Don't forget to tell 'em, Sheriff, that what you saw was a *youngster*—a boy.

SHERIFF: Well, he was anyways fifteen. Them Finches were *mean*, even that young.

92

|              | Seen anyway that it was my chance to grab a Finch. Governor told me not to come back without one, didn't he? So I stole up on the young feller and said: "Howdy, young feller!" |
|--------------|--|
| YOUNG FINCH: | Huh? Say, who're you? |
| SHERIFF:     | Wal, I'm a new settler around these parts. Thought I'd come over and chin awhile with m' neighbors. |
| YOUNG FINCH: | Yeah? Well, mister, we don't want no neighbors. |
| SHERIFF:     | Aw now . . . now. Come over here and sit down. Let's talk, friendly-like. Put down your ax. |
| YOUNG FINCH: | I ain't supposed to talk to nobody but Finches. |
| SHERIFF:     | Wal, I'm a nice, friendly feller. Put down your ax and set a spell. You're tired. |
| YOUNG FINCH: | I ain't neither. No Finch ever gets tired! |
| SHERIFF:     | All right, you ain't tired, but come and talk just the same. Lay down your ax. There! That's right. And now, young feller! Put up your hands! |
| YOUNG FINCH: | Who? Me? Hey! You got a gun on me! |
| SHERIFF:     | Yes, you. And don't start fer *your* guns. |
| YOUNG FINCH: | I ain't got no guns! Just wait 'll I call my folks! Ma! Pa! |
| SHERIFF:     | Here! You shet up! You're the one beat |

93

up that Norwegian, ain't you? Sure you are. Get on this hoss! I'm takin' you to Madison. Climb on! Hurry.

YOUNG FINCH: Jest wait till my folks hears about this! They'll fill your hide so full o' holes. . .!

SHERIFF: That's what I'm skeered of. Governor, here we come!

BALLAD SINGER: The Finches they heard
The youngster yell.
They grabbed their hosses
And rode like—

FARMER: Well, they rode *fast* anyway!

BALLAD SINGER: The Sheriff was so skeered when he reached an inn,
That he hollered for the keeper
To lock him in!

SHERIFF: Hey, Innkeeper! Innkeeper!

INNKEEPER: Yas. Vat you vant?

SHERIFF: Innkeeper, I'm Sheriff Bird from Madison. You got any place here where I can hide? I got a prisoner, too.

INNKEEPER: Vat? You vant to *hide?* You, der sheriff?

SHERIFF: The Finches are after me.

INNKEEPER: Ah, dot iss different. Der Finches, zay vill cud you up in liddle pieces and use you for ferdilizer on garten.

SHERIFF: I know it. What'll I do? I can't keep ahead of 'em much longer.

INNKEEPER: I tell you. From here, Lake Mills, dere iss two roads to Madison. Vun new road. Vun old road. You take der *new* road. Ven Finches coom I tell dem you take *old* road.

SHERIFF: Innkeeper, you're a good citizen. You've saved the sheriff's hide! Come on here, young Finch! Get movin'. Goodbye, Innkeeper! We can use a man like you in the Wisconsin Government! Run fer somethin' next election! We're off!

BALLAD SINGER: When the Sheriff got back
To Madison Town,
He yelled for the Governor
To come on down.
His prisoner to the ground he swung.
Governor said, "Sheriff, he's pretty young!"

SHERIFF: Yep. He's young, Governor. But he's mean, too.

GOVERNOR: He ain't hardly weaned, Sheriff. But he'll do, sir. Let me congratulate you, Sheriff. You're the only man that ever captured a Finch!

"Seems to me," I say, "that there ought to be some yarns about the good things the Finches did. Most every outlaw we ever had had a good side to him, so they say."

**95**

"We're comin' to that," says the farmer. "Sing the verse about the preacher, neighbor!"

BALLAD SINGER: Was a new preacher
Come to the town.
Earnest young feller
In a new black gown.
Country boys thought they'd have some fun,
So they went to camp meetin', preacher fer to run!

"That's right," says the farmer, "and here's the preacher now!"

PREACHER: I'm George Williams, Methodist preacher. Came here to Wisconsin Territory in 1840; just a young fellow, not really dry behind the ears yet, as they say. I knew it was rough country, and I'd heard about the Finches. I guess I thought maybe I could do 'em some good. Strangely enough, though, the Finches never showed up for church. I never saw them at all. But there was a rough local element that caused me lots of trouble. Seven or eight big rough young men that'd sit right down on the front rows and yell and holler when I started to preach.

Brothers and Sisters, my text today . . .

A RUFFIAN: Yipee! That's tellin' em!

ANOTHER: Give it to 'em, Parson!

PREACHER: And they'd keep hollering and heckling me till I'd have to stop talking, and the decent members of my congregation'd all go away. I didn't know what to do. Well, one Sunday my congregation—what there was left of it—had assembled, and the rough young men were there in the front seats waiting to heckle me as usual.

A RUFFIAN: We'll finish this preacher today!

ANOTHER: We'll run him out of town today all right!

PREACHER: When suddenly I saw some of the girls who were sitting up in front craning their necks to look around at the back door. I could hear the girls whispering:

A GIRL: Look! Isn't he *handsome!*

HER FRIEND: He's *big*, too! Look at his shoulders! Who is he?

PREACHER: And there, sitting on the back row, was the handsomest man I've ever seen in my life. Yes, and one of the biggest too. He was well-dressed and clean. Quietly waiting for the service to begin.

I began to preach: Brothers and Sisters, my text for today is from the Chapter of St. Luke. "There was, in the days of Herod . . ."

A RUFFIAN: Hey, preacher! What was that?

ANOTHER: Yeah, preacher. Talk louder, can't you?

PREACHER: I could see that the same old thing was going to happen again. When suddenly that stranger in the back of the audience stood up. He towered over the whole congregation. He walked down the aisle, and as he walked, he pulled two large pistols from under his coat. I didn't know what was going to happen. I waited for the stranger to point his weapons at me, but instead, he stopped at the front row and looked at the rowdies who were causing all the trouble—just stood and looked at them. And as he stood there, they sank down in their seats and were silent. Then the stranger spoke:—

STRANGER: This is holy ground, where men come to worship their God. The tavern and the saloon were created for the rough humor of dregs like yourselves! Now! On your feet!

PREACHER: And the rowdies rose as one man!

STRANGER: March on! Line up in front of the pulpit! Hurry!

A Ruffian:    Sure, sure, mister . . .

Another:      Anything you say, mister.

Stranger:     Now. Kneel down, all of you. Kneel I say!

Preacher:     And they did kneel! Seven big, strapping fellows kneeling down in front of my pulpit. Then the stranger looked at me and said:

Stranger:     Parson, you may now preach this skum a sermon, and I'm here to see that it does 'em some good! They're going to kneel here until you finish, and personally I hope you preach a mighty *long* sermon. And one thing more before you begin, you other folks that believe this young man deserves a better deal than he's had around here, better take over from now on. See that this rough element is kept in its place; and let the Gospel be spoken as it should be—with freedom in the speakin'! Proceed, Parson!

Preacher:     And that day I preached a four-hour sermon, and the stranger kept those men kneeling for every bit of it. And when it was over, the stranger slipped out the door; and everywhere folks were saying:—

A Lady:       A marvelous sermon!

Her Husband:  Magnificent! But who was the stranger?

A Neighbor:    Who *was* he? Why, didn't you know? That was Ben Finch. The best shot and the greatest hoss thief in Wisconsin!

"You haven't told me a thing about the Finch women," I say to the farmer. "The Finch men seem to have been plenty active, but how about the gals?"

"There was one Finch gal that was a beauty," says the farmer. "That was Patsy Finch. And her beauty was more'n skin deep, too. Sing us a verse," he says to the Ballad Singer. "Sing us a verse of your song about pretty Patsy Finch."

Ballad Singer: A settler's wife
She once fell ill;
There wasn't no help
To be had until
Patsy Finch on her big black steed,
Came flyin' along with a kindly deed!

"Over here's Hank Jones," says the farmer. "He'll tell you about Patsy. Amble up here on the doorstep, Hank."

Henry Jones:    My name's Hank Jones all right. Settled out in this Wisconsin country in 1841. Had a tough time gettin' started. Bugs were bad the first year, and it rained me out the second. My wife, Mary, was frail too. The pioneer country was hard on her.

|  |  |
|---|---|
|  | Well, long about April 1843, Mary fell sick. Real sick. Just lay there, quiet and pale, like she was gonna die. |
| I: | What'd you do, Hank? |
| HENRY JONES: | Almost out of my mind, mister. You see, I couldn't leave her, and there wasn't anybody livin' close. Not like you folks nowadays, when you can pick up a telephone, no sir. I didn't know what to do. Mary seemed to be gettin' weaker and weaker, and I thought certain I was gonna lose her, when suddenly I heard the sound of a hoss gallopin'. I ran to the door, and there, flyin' across the flatlands below my cabin, was a sight I'll never forget. No sir! It was a girl on a tall black hoss, her hair flyin' out behind, and in the evenin' light seemed like somethin' not of the earth at all, but like the fairy women you read about. Well, she rode right up to the door and called to me: |
| PATSY FINCH: | You! Hank Jones! |
| HENRY JONES: | I'm Hank Jones. |
| PATSY FINCH: | Is your wife sick? |
| HENRY JONES: | Why, yeah! Yes, she is. |
| PATSY FINCH: | I'm coming in. |
| HENRY JONES: | How . . . how'd you know Mary was sick? Who are you? |

PATSY FINCH: I know lots of things other people don't know. I'm Patsy Finch. Now, where's your wife?

HENRY JONES: She's . . . in here. She's awful sick, Miss . . .

PATSY FINCH: She certainly is. Just skin and bones.

HENRY JONES: Well, we had hard times, Miss. Nothin' to eat much this year.

PATSY FINCH: Out on my saddle you'll find a leather bag, Hank. It's got some broth in it. You bring that broth in here and heat it up on the stove.

HENRY JONES: All right, Miss.

I: Did the broth help your wife, Hank?

HENRY JONES: It did. Patsy stayed with Mary all night and part of the next day. She had medicine too. And when Patsy left, Mary was able to talk a little bit. And do you know what, mister? The mornin' after Patsy left I found a lot of food and a little bag of money on my doorstep. You can say what you want about the Fightin' Finches, but I'm not gonna believe it unless it's *good* you say of 'em. Patsy Finch saved Mary's life, and the start that bit of money gave me, made me able to weather through a hard year. The next year was better, and after awhile I was on my feet. I owe that to Patsy Finch.

"That's a right touching tale," I say as Hank Jones finishes. "But I guess the Finches could afford to be kind sometimes."

"They could that," replies the farmer. "They stole plenty. And if my neighbor'll sing a final verse . . ."

BALLAD SINGER: The Finches were bold.
 The Finches were bad.
 They're not here now,
 And we oughta be glad.
 But one thing certain you must agree,
 The Finches were the worst in the whole countree!

". . . we'll be sayin' goodbye, for now. And anytime you want to know more about the Fightin' Finches, just ask *us*. So long!"

## INVENTOR . . .

### on my doorstep

INVENTIONS by Wisconsin men have had a very marked effect on our national life. Imagine the plight of American womanhood without the typewriter—an invention of Christopher Lathom Sholes, of Milwaukee. Or imagine the American Farmer struggling along without the twine binder—an invention of John Appleby, of La Grange.

Grain cutting, in the days before the Appleby invention, was a tough, hard process. Picture a couple of Wisconsin farm boys cradling a field of wheat, sometime, say, about

104

1840. All the conversation in rhythm with the swings of the cradle.

"Hard goin', Bill," says Harry.

"Yep."

"Slow work, Bill."

"Yep," says Bill swinging as he talks.

"Hot, Bill. My back's busted."

"Yep."

"Like to bust this cradle into a million pieces. Wouldn't you?"

"Yep."

"Can't you say nothin' but *yep?*"

"Nope."

"You reckon they'll ever invent somethin' that'll cut grain and tie it without this here cradlin'? You reckon, Bill?"

"Nope."

"Ain't it dinnertime, Bill?"

"Nope."

But those boys cradling grain in that Wisconsin field in the 1840's couldn't know that in New York State, yes, maybe on that very same summer day, a family was getting aboard an Erie Canal packet boat—the Appleby family. Pa Appleby,* Ma Appleby, and Johnny.

"Pa," shouts Johnny.

"Yes, son?"

---

* Some condensation of fact has been made in this yarn. Appleby Sr. died when John was about ten. In this story Pa is meant to represent John's real father, a stepfather, and neighbors—the Houghtons—who were kind to him.

"Just where we goin', Pa?"

"Goin' out to Wisconsin, son!"

"And we're stayin' out there?"

"Sure, son. Lots of York State folks are goin' out to Wisconsin."

"And where is Wisconsin, Pa?" asks Johnny.

"Oh, out West there, somewhere."

"Don't ask so many questions, son," says Ma Appleby.

"You're the askin'est boy I ever saw!"

"Pa," cries Johnny, "here comes the boat captain!"

"Get aboard, folks. Get aboard," says the Captain.

"Captain," asks Johnny, "does this boat go all the way to Wisconsin? How fast does it go? Don't the mules that pull the boat ever get tired? Where are we gonna sleep?"

"You'll find out, son," laughs the Captain. "Get aboard now."

"Come on, sonny," says Ma.

And Johnny Appleby, like so many other York State folks, came up the old Erie Canal, slow and easy, listenin' to the clinkin' harness chains, hearin' the canal songs!

> *Oh the E-ri-e was arisin'*
> *The gin was gettin' low;*
> *And I don't suppose I'll get a drink,*
> *Till we get to Buffalo!*

And it was through the old Erie, the Lakes, and to Wisconsin. Milwaukee: low, marshy, the streets filled with Indians, teamsters. Different indeed from the small, neat milling towns the Applebys had left in New York State. In Milwaukee, too, the Appleby family faced the grave problem of finding transportation West. Pa was worried. "Ma," he said, "I don't know what we're going to do. We've got no wagon. No horses. If I'd known what Wisconsin was like . . ."

"Cheer up, Pa," Ma said. "Somethin'll turn up. Look! Here comes Johnny, and there's a stranger with him. Who do you suppose . . . ?"

"Ma! Pa!" shouted Johnny. "Here's Mr. Esterly."

"Who?"

The tall stranger with Johnny laughed and bowed to Ma. "The boy's right," he said. "My name's *Esterly*. George Esterly. I found your son over by the hotel yonder. He introduced himself."

"Pa," said Johnny. "Mr. Esterly's got a big wagon, and he's goin' on West. Says we can all ride with him. I asked him, Pa."

"*You* asked him?" cried Pa.

"Johnny," said Ma. "You shouldn't have . . ."

"Why, that's all right, ma'am," said George Esterly. "Matter of fact I was lookin' for company. It's a long ride out to Walworth County."

"Walworth County?" asked Pa. "Say, is there a town named La Grange out there?"

"Sure is. Or what passes for a town. That where you folks are headed?"

"Yes. We got friends from New York State out there. Harris family."

"Know 'em well," said George Esterly. "Now this is right nice! You bring your things over to my wagon, and we'll get started. Reckon us men'll have to walk a part of the way. Roads are real bad."

"I don't mind walking all the way, Mr. Esterly," said Pa, "as long as my family can ride."

"Well, I don't have too much load. Just packin' a few things for myself. I been trying to invent a reaper, you see; something to save cutting grain by cradle. Needed more tools and supplies. Well, let's get started. And say, Appleby, that's a bright boy of yours. Smart's a dollar! Yes, sir!"

So in Walworth County, Wisconsin, the Applebys settled down. Found the land good; raised fine crops; and Johnny grew up.

One summer when Johnny was about fifteen years old, there was a big crop of wheat to harvest. Johnny and his Pa were sharpening up the big cradles getting them ready to swing into the ripe grain. "Mine's sharp's a whistle, Pa," said Johnny.

"Give the blade a few more licks, Johnny. Can't have a cradle blade too sharp."

"All right, Pa." Johnny whetted the blade for a little while. "Pa?"

"Yes, son?"

"Do you suppose George Esterly will ever get his reaper finished?"

"Don't know, son. George's been working on that reaper for a long while."

"Pa, someday *I'm* gonna invent a reaper."

"Get along with your sharpening, son."

"All right, Pa. But I'm gonna invent a reaper just the same. Pa," said Johnny pointing, "here comes George Esterly now."

"I declare," Pa said. "Over this way, George," he called, "over here by the barn!"

"Getting the cradles ready, eh?" George Esterly said, as he tied up his horse and came over to where Pa and Johnny were working. "You got a fine wheat crop, Appleby."

"Dead ripe," Pa said. "Should have started cutting yesterday."

"You ain't gonna need those cradles anymore, Appleby."

"How's that?"

"I finished my reaper, Appleby. She's ready to work."

"Glad to hear it."

"Was wonderin'," George said, "if I could try it out in your field?"

"Why . . . dunno," Pa said. "You think it'll work? Sure enough?"

" 'Course it'll work. 'Tis a wonderful machine, Appleby. Cut down your grain and lay it flat. Save all that heavy cradle swingin'. How about lettin' me try?"

"If you're sure it won't ruin my field."

"Guarantee it."

"Well then, come as early as you want to. Soon's the dew's off."

"There'll be history made in your wheat field tomorrow,

109

Appleby," said George Esterly. "Say, what's the boy lookin' so sour about?" he said, looking at Johnny. "Cheer up, son. Ain't you excited?"

"I was kind of figuring on inventing a reaper myself," Johnny said.

"What?" roared Esterly. "Now there's a boy for you, Appleby." He began to laugh. "There's a boy! Son," he cried, "maybe you *will* invent somethin' sure enough. But it won't be no reaper. No sir! I done *that* myself!"

Well, on the following morning a considerable crowd of people'd gathered in the Appleby field to watch the wonderful new reaper. A couple of the neighborhood boys were looking it over. "Quite a machine, ain't it, Bill?"

"Yep."

"Sure save us some work . . . *if it works,* won't it?"

"Yep."

"Guess it'll cut the grain and lay it flat. Better 'n cradlin', ain't it, Bill?"

"Yep."

"You reckon it'll work, Bill?"

"Nope. Don't reckon it will."

"Now folks," cried George Esterly, making a kind of speech. "Now folks, she's most ready to go. Stand back and give her plenty of room! You're gonna see somethin' you've never seen before. Wheat cut by reaper! No more back-breakin' work. You boys with the team there! You ready?"

"Ready, George."

"Then let's go!"

And with a big clatter the machine moved forward right into the wheat. The tall grain fell down behind the cutting bar in a flat swath.

"She's workin', boys!" shouted George Esterly. "She's workin'. My dream come true, boys! Twenty years I have been inventin' this reaper! An' there she goes! Johnny!" he roared, grabbing Johnny by the shirttail and swinging him up to his shoulder. "Johnny, what ye think of my reaper now? Think ye could do as well?"

"Mr. Esterly," said Johnny Appleby, "that's a good machine. But it'll not be complete until it ties the wheat into bundles and rakes them off!"

"There'll never be a machine that'll do that, boy!" He set Johnny down in the stubble and rushed off after his reaper. "There she goes! Look at 'er! Look at 'er cut!"

From that day on Johnny Appleby's hands and brain were busy with a task he'd set for himself: binding grain by machinery. Guess he must have spent considerable time on it, because his Ma and Pa were sometimes right worried.

MA:     Pa, I wish you'd speak to Johnny. He just sits around and broods. Really, Pa, I don't rightly understand Johnny anymore.

PA:     Just one thing on his mind, Ma. Notion of bindin' grain. Don't know how a boy o' mine ever got so fanciful.

MA:     He's not a bit like the other boys! Johnny's eighteen now. He ought to be payin' heed to girls, Pa.

**111**

PA: Annie Spink, fer instance?

MA: She's eatin' her heart out for Johnny, Pa. But he never seems to notice Annie at all. Why, I declare, Pa, when you were Johnny's age . . .

PA: Here comes Annie now. Howdy, Annie!

ANNIE: Hello, Mr. Appleby. Howdy, Mrs. Appleby. Ma sent you over some fresh butter, seein' how your cream ain't quite ready to churn an' all . . .

MA: Now that's right kind of your Ma, Annie. Tell her thanks, and I'll be sendin' *her* over some fresh bread. Guess you can take it back with you if you can wait till it's out of the oven.

ANNIE: I can wait. Where . . . where's Johnny?

PA: Johnny's out'n the orchard, Annie. He's supposed to be hoein' corn, but I reckon he's settin' out there under a tree dreamin'.

MA: S'pose you go out and visit with Johnny, Annie. 'Spect he'd be glad to see you, and maybe you can cheer 'im up.

ANNIE: I dunno, Mrs. Appleby. Johnny just don't . . .

MA: Now you run along. Johnny'll be glad to see you. I know he will.

ANNIE: Well, all right.

MA: Bread'll be ready for you when you get back.


So Annie went out to the orchard calling:

ANNIE: Johnny. Johnny!

JOHNNY: Here I am. Over here under the apple tree.

ANNIE: What're you doin'?

112

JOHNNY: Carvin'.

ANNIE: Carvin' what?

JOHNNY: Oh, I dunno. What do *you* want, Annie?

ANNIE: Why . . . I . . . I dunno. I just thought . . .

JOHNNY: I'm pretty busy.

ANNIE: You're not busy! Not one bit! You're supposed to be hoeing corn! You're just *loafin'*!

JOHNNY: I'm not loafing, Annie.

ANNIE: You are so! Maybe you don't know it, Johnny Appleby, but folks around here are beginning to call you just a lazy loafer!

JOHNNY: Look Annie! Look what I'm doin'! I think I got it!

ANNIE: Got what?

JOHNNY: My knotter for tyin' the twine. Look! I carved it out of this piece of apple wood. See? Looks like a bird's beak, and when it opens, it'll grab the twine, like this, and pull it through and . . .

ANNIE: Oh, you and your old twine binder! Johnny, why do you just go on and on, dreamin' about somethin' that's just impossible? Why'nt you sing and dance and have fun like the rest of us?

"I've got it!" cried Johnny. "It'll work! I know it will!" He jumped up and started running toward the house. "Ma! Pa!"

"Johnny," Annie called. "Where are you goin'? Come back here!"

"Ma! Pa!" yelled Johnny. "Come out and see! Quick!"

**113**

"What is it, son," said Pa, running off the porch to meet Johnny with Ma right behind him. "What's the matter?"

"Pa, look! See? I've tied the knot!"

"What've you done, son?"

"Tied the knot. See?"

"You mean, you 'n Annie've," began Ma. "Oh, Johnny ..."

"That's fine, son. Fine," Pa said. "Annie's a *fine* girl!"

"I don't mean Annie," said Johnny. "I mean my knotter for the twine binder. It works! I've got it this time!"

"Oh, son!" Ma said. She shook her head in disgust and went into the house.

But Johnny's first knotter for the dream binder was just a beginning. There was a lot to be done: the compression of the bundles of grain after they were cut; the elevating of the grain to the knotter; these were weighty mechanical problems for a young fellow Johnny's age. And then, of course, there was the Civil War.

Johnny volunteered one day, and his Ma and Pa and some of the others from around the neighborhood were there to see him march away. "Goodbye, son," Ma said. "Come back to us."

"I will, Ma. Don't cry, Ma. Goodbye, Pa!"

" 'Bye, son," Pa said. "Take care of yourself."

"Here's Annie, son," Ma said. "Aren't you going to say goodbye to Annie?"

" 'Bye, Annie," Johnny said. "Well, I got to be goin'."

"Wait a minute, Johnny," said Annie. "Johnny, do you suppose, when you get back, that you ..."

"Bet your life," said Johnny. "When I get back I'll invent that twine binder sure as you're born, Annie. Got all the plans for it in my head now. When I get back . . ."

"Oh, Johnny!" Annie said. She started to cry, but Johnny didn't seem to notice.

Johnny came back from the Civil War one summer day. He didn't collect any hero's medals,* but he fought all the way through just the same. His Ma and Pa were there to see him come home to La Grange, Wisconsin.

"Ma! Pa!" cried Johnny. "I'm so glad to see you, Ma . . ."

"We're glad to see you, son," said Ma. "Johnny, you look mighty thin! You come home this minute! You need a square meal!"

"Wait, Ma. Where's Annie?" Johnny asked, looking around.

"She's standin' over there by herself. Better go see her, son."

"Annie's been waitin' for you, Johnny," Pa said.

"I want to see her," Johnny said. He walked over to where she was standing. "Hello, Annie."

"Hello, Johnny."

"You glad to see me, Annie?"

"Sure," said Annie. "You glad to see me?"

"Thought about you all through the War," Johnny said. "Guess I never treated you very well. Look, Annie," he

* He did, however, whittle out an important magazine-load device for rifles.

said taking his hand out of his pocket. "I brought you somethin'. A ring. Made it myself."

"A ring? For me?"

" 'Taint much," Johnny said. "Just a ring carved out of a button. Lots of us made 'em."

"It's pretty," Annie said. "Does it mean that you'n I are. . . ?"

"I kind of figured on it like that," Johnny said.

"You still dreamy and far away like you used to be?"

"I dunno. Guess I've changed some."

"You want me more'n that twine binder you was always dreamin' about?"

"I guess so," Johnny said.

"Is your name Johnny Appleby?" asked a stranger coming up behind Johnny and putting his hand on his shoulder.

"Yeah, it is," Johnny said, turning slowly away from Annie. "What do you want?"

"My name's Parker," the stranger said. It was a hot day, and he kept wiping the sweat out of his eyes with a red handkerchief. "I'm from Beloit. I heard you was making some progress with a twine binder invention before the War. You see, Appleby, I own a machine shop in Beloit, and I been interested in trying to get out a new binder machine. I was wonderin', Appleby, whether you'd like to work with me?"

"I guess I would," Johnny said. "Sure I would, Mr. Parker. Let's go some place where we can talk."

"But Johnny!" cried Annie. "Come back!"

" 'Bye, Annie," Johnny said. He went to her and put

116

his hand on her arm. "I was wrong, Annie. I got to invent this binder before I do anything else. But I'll be back soon's I do. Bet your life I will!"

" 'Bye, Johnny," Annie said. She turned and walked away very fast.

"We can talk over here in the shade of the wagon, Mr. Parker," said Johnny. "What kind of a binder do you have in mind?"

"A binder that will tie grain. Cut it and tie it. There's been talk of a wire binder—usin' wire to tie the bundles."

"Wire's no good," Johnny said.

"Why not?"

"For a lot of reasons. But mainly because wire will get mixed up with the straw, and cattle'll eat it. It'll kill cattle, Parker."

"Nonsense!"

"I'm positive, Mr. Parker, that a *twine* binder's the solution."

"Do you want to work with me, Appleby?"

"I do," said Johnny, "but . . ."

"Then you'll work on a *wire* binder," Mr. Parker said. "I will put up the money. The inventions are in your hands."

"I'll work with you," said Johnny, "but if the wire binder proves worthless, will you back me in inventing a *twine* binder?"

"You get us a wire binder first. We'll talk about the other later."

Johnny did invent a wire binder, and it was a good one,

117

as wire binders went. On the trial it worked fine, except that the farmer, John Dates, whose field they tried the binder in, didn't like the wire on the bundles. "I don't want you to cut my field with that contraption," Dates said.

"Why not, Mr. Dates?" asked Parker. "Ain't the binder working all right?"

"It's workin', yes. But that wire'll kill my stock. I don't want it in the straw!"

"But, Mr. Dates. . . ," began Parker.

"Get the machine out of my field," Dates said. "And you won't find another farmer in the country'll let you cut his fields with a wire binder."

"What'll we do, Appleby?" asked Parker.

"Looks as if I was right about the wire binder, Mr. Parker."

"Maybe you were, Appleby. We can't make a binder farmers won't use. That's certain."

"I could make a twine binder, Mr. Parker."

"Nope," Parker said, "I've sunk enough money in this blamed binder business already. I'm ready to quit. Pull the binder out of the field. Let's go home."

So things drifted along for awhile. Johnny stayed in Beloit, and after awhile rumors began to drift in of other firms who had manufactured *wire* binders. They were being sued for the price of dead cattle killed by eating wire. News came of explosions in flour mills caused by wire coming in contact with the grinding machinery. Men were killed.

Johnny couldn't take much pleasure in this further proof of his judgment. He was dejected; spent some time studying plans for his twine binder, but for the most part, he dreamed and drifted. Didn't do much of anything.

One day he met Parker and another man on the street. "Hello, Appleby," said Parker. "Where've you been?"

"Studying," Johnny said. "Studying plans for that twine binder."

Parker turned to the other man. "Appleby, I want you to meet Mr. Smith. He's representing Gammon and Deering, harvester people."

"Glad to know you, Mr. Smith."

"Same to you, Appleby," Smith said. "Parker's been telling me about your twine binder idea."

"What do you think of it?" asked Johnny.

"I think it's crazy. For one thing, the crickets will eat the twine off the bundles."

"I don't think so," Johnny said.

"Well, I do, young man. But do you know what I told Parker? I said, 'Parker, this man has an idea. Sounds crazy, but you better back him!'"

"And I will," said Mr. Parker. "I'll put up the money, Appleby. You get over to the shop and start work. You hear?"

"It'll take some time, Mr. Parker," Johnny said. "It'll be a big job."

"Well, speed it up!"

"I will," Johnny said. "I'll do my best. I sure will!"

Every so often Parker would drop into Johnny's workroom at the machine shop. "Been two months, Appleby," he would say. "How are you coming?"

"Working parts are in order. But I have to mount 'em on a frame."

"Well, speed it up!"

Or another time when Parker dropped in he mentioned that it had been six months and that Appleby didn't seem to be making any progress at all. "Lots of problems, Mr. Parker," Johnny replied. "Had to work it out so all the parts of the binder get power from the wheels. Had to invent an elevator too, to carry the bundles of grain up to the knotter."

And finally when a year had passed, Parker entered Johnny's room, looked around at the scattered parts of the binder, and remarked, "This contraption looks like it did six months ago. You haven't been making *any* progress. Been lyin' down, Appleby?"

"Mr. Parker," Johnny said, "what you're looking at here are the parts of the model. The *complete binder* is now down in the polishing room. Mr. Parker, it's ready to go!"

A few days later Johnny's binder was out in a wheat field near Beloit, ready for trial. A lot of folks were looking it over.

"This binder looks some different, don't it, Bill?"

"Yep."

"Got some parts I reckon those others didn't have."

"Yep."

120

"You reckon Johny Appleby's binder'll work, Bill?"

"Yep, I reckon she will!"

"Folks," said Parker. "This is the first binder in the world that will cut grain and tie it with twine. Johnny Appleby invented it. Johnny's been dreamin' for a long time about this contraption, and if it works today it'll mark a turning point in the whole history of farmin'. And now we're gonna try it! You there," he yelled to the driver of the team, "you ready?"

"Ready," replied the driver.

"Then let her go!"

The driver spoke to his horses, and the binder clattered its way into the grain.

"She's workin', Bill," cried Harry. "Look at her kick them bundles out! Ain't that wonderful, Bill?"

"Yep."

"Well, Appleby," said Mr. Parker as the excitement died down, "your dream come true. Wait," he said as Johnny turned away, "where you goin'?"

"I just thought of something, Mr. Parker," Johnny said. "There's a girl I left back home. I gotta go and see her."

And that's almost the end of the story of this inventor on my doorstep. The big harvester companies were soon coming around, and all of 'em had to use Johnny's patents. I guess every binder in the world today uses some of Johnny Appleby's inventions. That first twine knotter he carved out in the orchard has never been improved on.

When Johnny got home he found the folks waiting for him.

**121**

"Johnny!" said Ma.

"Ma! Pa! I'm glad to be home! Where's Annie?"

"She's here, son. Waitin' for you, like always."

"Hello, Johnny," said Annie.

"Howdy, Annie."

"I'm still wearin' the ring you carved for me. See?"

"Yeah," Johnny said. "I could buy you a better one now, though."

"I don't want a better one."

"Come on to dinner," Ma said. "Come to dinner, everybody!"

# MUSKIE...

## on my doorstep

THE fishermen on my doorstep make a lot of fuss about a fish: the Muskellunge. They have endowed this fish with all sorts of unusual characteristics, and up in the Northern parts of the State, you're likely to hear very little except conversation about Muskies and Muskie fishing. The Muskie's a mighty famous citizen up around Hayward, or Eagle River, or Minocqua.

The hero qualities of this fish will emerge in any ordinary conversation. Suppose, for instance, that you are talking with two or three old-timers in the North Wisconsin country. Here's the way the chatter might go:

1ST OLD-TIMER: I'll tell you! Muskie's the fiercest thing they is!

2ND OLD-TIMER: That's right. He's vicious.

3RD OLD-TIMER: Got a sense o' humor all the same.

1ST OLD-TIMER: That's right! Take a sucker, he will, and toss it right up in the air! Play with it jest like a cat'll play with a mouse.

ALL: That's so!

2ND OLD-TIMER: (*to you*) See that island out there, son? Well sir, that island used to be farther over. Fisherman got a line on a Muskie he did, had to tie his line to a tree on that island to hold him. Muskie pulled that island 'bout a hundred yards.

3RD OLD-TIMER: They's a big Muskie lays right out there off the boat dock. Got one red eye and one green eye he has! When that red eye's showin' you dassant go out in a boat. No sir!

1ST OLD-TIMER: Paul Bunyan planted them Muskies in Wisconsin. Had one fer a pet, he did. Used to ride him around Big Spider Lake. Bet your life!

So, in honor of Muskie fishermen everywhere—myself included—I present now a little opera with a strictly all-

water cast, and starring the toughest of all the Wisconsin
Muskies: *Marbert, the Mad Muskellunge!* Here he is...

MARBERT:    Oh... I'm Marbert, the Mad Muskellunge.
Yes, I'm Marbert, the Mad Muskellunge.
When the fish see me comin',
They really start swimmin';
I'm Marbert, the Mad Muskellunge!

Oh... a sucker is my favorite dish.
I like him the best of all fish.
He's not much of a swimmer,
But he's very good dinner.
I'm Marbert, the Mad Muskellunge!

SUCKER:    Oh... I'm Tucker, the river-mud sucker.
Yes, I'm Tucker, the river-mud sucker.
It would be very rude
To say I'm no good...
I'm Tucker, the river-mud sucker.

MARBERT:    Tomorrow I'll eat you for lunch,
Or... maybe I'll have you for brunch.
You look very succulent
And not very truculent.
I'm Marbert, the Mad Muskellunge.

SUCKER:    But someday I'll have my revenge,
All my injuries I will avenge;
Some day when you're dinin',
A line will start windin'!
I'm Tucker, the river-mud sucker.

**125**

FISHERMAN:     I'm Dan, the old fisherman.
               Yes, I'm Dan, the old fisherman.
               I've been fishin' the lake
               For a Muskie to take
               Almost since my name has been Dan!

               I've tried and I've tried and I've tried;
               I've wept and I've sighed and I've cried;
               I've tried to catch Marbert
               From port and from starboard.
               I'm Dan, the old fisherman.

               Oh . . . I've tried every trick in the book
               For Marbert the Muskie to hook;
               And that is the reason
               I fish out of season!
               Yes, Marbert has made me a crook!

               If I could but think of a means,
               I would give every cent in my jeans,
               To have Marbert come stealin'
               A lure I am reelin'.
               I'm Dan, the old fisherman.

ALL FISH:      Oh . . . it's Marbert, the Mad Muskellunge!

MARBERT:       When through the blue water I plunge,
               The fishes they hear me
               And all of 'em fear me!
               I'm Marbert, the Mad Muskellunge!

I'm Marbert, the Mad Muskellunge!
All previous records expunge.
I'm the biggest and fiercest,
The fastest and worstest!
I'm Marbert, the Mad Muskellunge!

TURTLE: I'm Myrtle, the Spider Lake turtle.
Yes, I'm Myrtle, the Spider Lake turtle.
I've known Marbert for long,
And he's always done wrong.
I'm Myrtle, the Spider Lake turtle.

Whenever I'd see a fine fish,
There would be a mighty big swish!
And Marbert would grab it
Before I could nab it;
It got to be more than a habit!

ALL FISH: Oh . . . he's Marbert, the Mad Muskellunge!

MARBERT: When out of the water I plunge . . .

ALL FISH: The fishes they hear him,
And all of 'em fear him.
He's Marbert, the Mad Muskellunge!

SUCKER: Say, Marbert, how'd they happen to call
you the "Mad Muskellunge"?

**127**

MARBERT: You've asked for quite a long tale.
Of sex, of course, I am male.
I don't wanta bore ye,
But here is my story . . .
You won't find none like it at Yale.

ALL FISH: Oh . . . he's Marbert, the Mad Muskellunge!
He's Marbert, the Mad Muskellunge . . .

MARBERT: Of course I was hatched from an egg.
My mother's name, it was Peg.
Never heard o' my father
But that is no bother;
I'm Marbert, the Mad Muskellunge.

Oh, when I was just one inch long . . .

MA: Marbert! Marbert!

MARBERT: Yes, Ma?

MA: You come back here this minute! A blue
heron'll get you sure!

MARBERT: Aw, I ain't afraid of nothin'.

MA: All right! But you wait and see.

MARBERT: I'm hungry.

128

MA: Well, you know what to do.

WATER FLEA: I'm Dee, a small water flea.
Yes, I'm Dee, a small water flea.
When Marbert was hungry
(And he always was hungry),
He always came up after me!
Ow!

ALL FISH: Oh . . . he's Marbert, the Mad Muskellunge!
Yes, he's Marbert, the Mad Muskellunge!

MARBERT: Well, when I was *four* inches long,
My Ma she sang just one song;
She often did scold,
And quite often told
That my manner of living was wrong.

MA: Marbert! Marbert, do you hear me?

MARBERT: Naw! I don't hear you, Ma!

MA: You're the most headstrong fingerling I
ever saw.
You'll come to a bad end. Wanderin' all
over by yourself. Chasin' everything!

MARBERT: I'm *mean*, Ma! I'm the meanest thing in
the lake. I'm hungry!

MA: Well, go catch yourself some minnows.

MINNOW: Oh . . . I'm Tinno, the tender young minnow.
Yes, I'm Tinno, the tender young minnow.
In his terrible greed,
On me he would feed
Beneath the winnowing billow.

ALL FISH: Oh . . . he's Marbert, the Mad Muskellunge.
It's through the water he'll plunge.

FROG: I'm Hogg, the big bull frog.
I sit upon a log.
If I let Marbert catch me,
He surely will fetch me—
He loves nothing better than frog.
The dog!

ALL FISH: Oh . . . he's Marbert, the Mad Muskellunge.
Yes, he's Marbert, the Mad Muskellunge!

MARBERT: The fishes they hear me
And all of 'em fear me!
I'm Marbert, the Mad Muskellunge!

DUCK: I'm Cluck, the delicate duck.
Yes, I'm Cluck, the delicate duck.
When I'm eating a root
Marbert catches my foot!
I wish him all kinds of bad luck!

ALL FISH: Yes . . . he's Marbert, the Mad Muskellunge.
Oh . . . he's Marbert, the Mad Muskellunge!

CRAWDAD:    I'm Sad, the old crawdad.
Yes, I'm Sad, the old crawdad.
Marbet once ate my daughter
In two feet of water,
And that's why I'm feeling so sad!

ALL FISH:    He's Marbert, the Mad Muskellunge!

BATHING
BEAUTY:    I'm Lutie, the young bathing beauty.
And bathing is surely my duty.
Marbert bit off my toe
And nipped me below
And spoiled all my beautiful beauty!

ALL FISH:    Oh ... he's Marbert, the Mad Muskellunge.
Yes, he's Marbert, the Mad Muskellunge!

SUCKER:    I'm Tucker, the river-mud sucker.
Yes, I'm Tucker, the river-mud sucker.
It would be very rude
To say I'm no good;
I'm Tucker, the river-mud sucker.

Now listen, ye poor martyred fishes,
Ye frogs and ye beautiful misses,
Things have come to a pass
Where we must stand en masse,
And try to make Marbert less vicious!
(*Shouting*) Are you with me?

**131**

ALL FISH:    We're with you, Sucker, one hundred per cent!

SUCKER:      Then here's my plan:
             Over yonder's a mighty blue heron
             And into the water he's starin'.
             We'll practice deceit
             No heron he'll beat,
             He'll be Marbert, the *gone* Muskellunge!

ALL FISH:    What'll we do, Sucker?

SUCKER:      Here's the plan: Duck, the heron won't eat you. You swim over near him and call to Marbert.

DUCK:        Here I go! (*Calling*) Marbert! Wouldn't you like nice tender young duck for supper? Yoo-hoo! Come and get me!

MARBERT:     Here I come, Duck!
             For . . . I'm Marbert, the Mad Muskellunge.
             When through the water I plunge;
             Here's a tender young duck!
             It's extremely good luck!
             I'm Marbert, the Mad Muskellunge!

DUCK:        Here I am, Marbert! Yoo-hoo! (*Softly*) Mr. Heron! There comes your dinner: a fat young Muskellunge!

HERON:    Oh, I'm Karen, the big blue heron,
          And it's mighty long legs I'm awearin',
          But when I'm standin' still,
          I rely on my bill
          To fill the inside of this heron!

          Oh, I see a young Muskie aswimmin',
          And a careless song he's ahummin',
          But he doesn't know
          That when I let go
          It's inside my stomach he's comin'.
          (*Shouting*) Hey there! Muskie!

MARBERT:  Were you addressing me?

HERON:    That I was, son. Come over here.

MARBERT:  I'm Marbert, the Mad Muskellunge,
          And under you I will scrunge.
          You may be a heron,
          But me you ain't scarin'!
          I'm Marbert, the Mad Muskellunge!

HERON:    Why, you little . . . Take that!

MARBERT:  Hah! Missed me! And you, Heron! Take
          that!

HERON:    Ouch! He bit me! Bit on the leg by a fish!
          This is news! News! He *is* mad! The Mad
          Muskellunge! I'll take this up with the

133

Assembly of Blue Herons. We'll omit young
Muskies from our choice list of delicacies!
News! News!

ALL FISH:    Oh, he's Marbert, the Mad Muskellunge!

SUCKER:    Foiled again!

MARBERT:    When into the water I plunge!

ALL FISH:    The fishes they hear him,
And all of 'em fear him.
He's Marbert, the Mad Muskellunge!

MARBERT:    Well, Ma, I fixed that ol' heron!
He won't be back!

MA:    Marbert, you'll be the death of me yet! You
willful, headstrong boy, you!

MARBERT:    I'm gonna be king! Nothin's too good for
Marbert.

MA:    The great fall hardest, Marbert. Marbert,
I think the time has come for you to know
a few of the facts of a fish's life.

MARBERT:    I know all the facts, Ma.

MA:    No, you don't, son. You see, you're thirty
inches long now. You're a big boy, Marbert.

134

MARBERT: I'll be bigger yet, Ma.

MA: Maybe—if you live long enough. Son, I asked your great great granddaddy to come and talk to you. He's lived a long while.

MARBERT: Aw . . . ol' fogy!

MA: Now, Marbert, be nice!

MARBERT: Well. Howdy, Granddad!

GRANDDAD: Howdy, son. I attribute my long life to the fact I ain't never hardly et nothin'. Mighty thin all m' life, but son, I'm alive! Nothin'll give you fishhookitis quicker 'n a big appetite! There ain't no cure for fishhookitis! Wanta look out, son. They'll trick you.

MARBERT: Who'll trick me, Granddad? Nobody's smarter 'n me!

GRANDDAD: Fishermen'll trick you, son.

MARBERT: I don't know what you mean. And I'm hungry again!

GRANDDAD: Hold on, son! You're thirty inches long now. Big enough to be caught. They'll be after you now!

MARBERT: Who'll be after me?

GRANDDAD: Well . . . listen!

FISHERMAN: I'm Dan the ol' fisherman!
Yes, I'm Dan, the ol' fisherman!
I've been fishin' the lake
For a Muskie to take
'Most since my name has been Dan!

Oh, I lace out my pretty new line
With a lure that is shiny and fine;
If a Muskie should strike it,
I surely would like it;
I'm sure that he'd like to be mine!

GRANDDAD: Hear that, son? That's ol' Dan. He's death
on Muskies. Won't fish for nothin' else.

MARBERT: I'm not afraid of 'im! What's that thing
he's throwin' into the water?

GRANDDAD: That's a lure, son. Looks like a fish, don't
it? But things ain't what they seem. Don't
grab it, Marbert! It's full o' fishhooks.

MARBERT: I *will* grab it! Marbert's the king o' the
lake! Here I go!

GRANDDAD: Marbert! Come back!

MARBERT: Oh, Dan thinks he is very smart,
But he don't know a mad Muskie's heart.
I'll grab his bait—
I ain't gonna wait!
I'll take this feller apart!
There!

FISHERMAN: Ah, hooked! A Muskie at last!
(*Singing*) I'll reel in my wonderful bait.
This time it ain't too late.
I've got him caught;
He must weigh a lot,
He pulls hard at any rate.

ALL FISH: He's Marbert, the Mad Muskellunge!

1ST VOICE: Lookut 'im pull!

2ND VOICE: See 'im fight!

SUCKER: We got Marbert now! Pull, Fisherman!

MARBERT: Oh, Dan thinks he has won the race,
But that is hardly the case.
Tied his line to a log
As big as a hog!
(*Yelling*) Now pull till you're black in the
face!

137

FISHERMAN:     Oh, he's a big one all right.
He certainly is hooked tight!
I'm pulling so hard,
I'm really right tard;
I'm pulling with all my might!

SOUND:     *CRACK!*
Oh, there! He has broken my pole!
Upon my very soul!
I had him on,
But now he is gone!
He's left me in a bad hole! (*Sobs*)

ALL FISH:     Oh, he's Marbert, the Mad Muskellunge!

MARBERT:     I've foxed ol' Dan,
The fisherman man.
I'm Marbert, the Mad Muskellunge!

SUCKER:     Escaped again! But we'll make a plot yet that'll fix ye!

MARBERT:     I'm king! King o' the Lake! Nobody plots against Marbert!

SUCKER:     All right, Marbert. But I'm tellin' you!

MARBERT:     Phooey!

ALL FISH:     Oh, he's Marbert, the Mad Muskellunge!
Yes, he's Marbert, the Mad Muskellunge!

SUCKER:     Oh, I'm Tucker, the river-mud sucker.
            Listen you fish and you mucker,
            We've failed in our plan,
            He's still not in the pan;
            We've got to be much more clever!
            Any ideas? You, Duck, you got an idea?

DUCK:       Not me.

SUCKER:     You, Minnow?

MINNOW:     I'm Tinno, the tender young minnow. I ain't
            ever had an idea.

SUCKER:     You, Frog?

FROG:       Who, me?

SUCKER:     Water Flea, you have an idea?

FLEA:       Nope.

SUCKER:     Crawdad, whatta you say?

CRAWDAD:    I'm Sad, the old crawdad.
            Yes, I'm Sad, the old crawdad.
            Marbert once ate my daughter
            In two feet of water,
            That's why I'm always so sad!
            I know what we must do!

**139**

ALL FISH:    What's that?

CRAWDAD:    Why, one of us must sacrifice himself to get Marbert.

SUCKER:     That's a fine idea! But who'll it be?

FLEA:       It won't be me, the Water Flea.

FROG:       It won't be Hogg, the big bull frog.

MINNOW:     It won't be Tinno, the tender young minnow.

DUCK:       It won't be Cluck, the delicate duck.

SUCKER:     Who, then?

ALL FISH:   *You*, then!

SUCKER:     *Me?* Tucker, the river-mud sucker?

ALL FISH:   Yes, you!
            You're Marbert's favorite dish.
            You're really not much of a fish!
            Not a very good swimmer,
            But mighty fine dinner.
            Marbert thinks you delish!

SUCKER:     You . . . you want me to sacrifice myself?

ALL FISH:    We'll build you a monument,
As big as a circus tent.
You'll be a hero
Greater than Nero,
You'll *never* pay any rent!

SUCKER:    Well, with housing like it is, I suppose I
might as well. What'll I do, Crawdad?

CRAWDAD:    Here is what you must do—
This is a scheme for two—
You must see ol' Dan
And make up a plan
That Marbert the Muskie will rue!

ALL FISH:    'Twill do! 'Twill do!

CRAWDAD:    Come here. Come here. Come here!
I'll whisper it in your ear:
Whis . . . whis . . . whis.
Whis . . . whis . . . whis.
Whis . . . whis . . . whis . . . whis , , , whis!

ALL FISH:    Oh, he's Marbert, the Mad Muskellunge.
Yes, he's Marbert, the Mad Muskellunge!

SUCKER:    I'm Tucker, the river-mud sucker.
Yes, I'm Tucker, the river-mud sucker.
I have a plan,
Mr. Fisherman Dan,
To give you old Marbert for supper!

FISHERMAN: You do, Sucker?
Come close to me, Sucker dear,
And whisper it into my ear.
Tell all your plan
To ol' Fisherman Dan,
And I'll give you a bottle of beer.

SUCKER: Then here is how you must sail—
You must do it this way or fail—
When tomorrow for lunch
On me Marbert would munch,
You will fasten your line to my tail!

ALL FISH: Hooray! Hooray! Hooray!
We've fixed mad Marbert today!
He'll never get away!
Hooray! Hooray! Hooray!
Oh, he's Marbert, the Mad Muskellunge.
Yes, he's Marbert, the Mad Muskellunge!

SUCKER: Marbert! Oh, Marbert!

MARBERT: Well, well, well! It's my old friend, the
sucker!
Oh, a sucker is my favorite dish
I love you the best of all fish.
You're not much of a swimmer,
But you're mighty fine dinner,
I know you are very delish!

142

SUCKER: Come and eat me, Marbert!

MARBERT: Oh, I think I will have you for lunch,
Or perhaps you will do for brunch.
You look very succulent
And not very truculent.
I'm Marbert, the Mad Muskellunge!
Are you ready, Sucker?

SUCKER: I'm ready. Goodbye. Goodbye!

ALL FISH: Goodbye, goodbye, goodbye!
We cannot help but sigh.
You're only a sucker
But now you must die!
Goodbye, goodbye, goodbye!

SUCKER: Goodbye.

ALL FISH: Goodbye, goodbye, goodbye!

SUCKER: Goodbye!

MARBERT: Hello, *Sucker!* Gulp!

ALL FISH: He's down! He's down! He's down!
He's won his golden crown!
The sucker's been swallowed,
Long may he be hallowed!
He's down, he's down, he's down!

MARBERT:    Are you there, Sucker?


SUCKER:     (*Distant*) I'm here, Marbert! And *you're
            hooked!* Who's the sucker, now?


ALL FISH:   He's Marbert, the Mad Muskellunge!
            Yes, he's Marbert, the Mad Muskellunge!
            He really looks fine
            On the end of a line!
            He's Marbert, the *hooked* Muskellunge!


FISHERMAN:  Oh, I am old Fisherman Dan.
            Try and escape if you can!
            I'm usin' a pole
            Big round as a bowl;
            Tonight you will be in the pan!


MARBERT:    I'm Marbert, the Mad Muskellunge.
            I plunge, and I lunge, and I plunge!
            I can't get loose,
            Though I pull like a moose.
            I'm Marbert, the Mad Muskellunge.


ALL FISH:   He pulls, he pulls, he pulls.
            He pulls like a pair o' mules!
            He walks on his tail,
            But to not much avail,
            It's no longer us that're fools!

MARBERT: I'm Marbert, the *Sad* Muskellunge.
No longer the Mad Muskellunge!
I thought I'd be luckier
Than caught by a sucker.
Why didn't I listen to Ma!

SUCKER: I told you I'd have my revenge!
My injuries all I'd avenge!
And when you were dinin',
A line *did* start windin'!
I'm Tucker, the river-mud sucker.

ALL FISH: Goodbye! Goodbye! Goodbye!
It's time to say goodbye.

MARBERT: Oh, I'm Marbert, the Mad Muskellunge.
Yes, I'm Marbert, the Mad Muskellunge!

ALL FISH: He's Marbert, the Mad Muskellunge!
A very difficult case!
But he'll really look fine,
When they're drinkin' their wine . . .
On a board above the fireplace!

# SHIPWRECK . . .

## *on my doorstep*

THE story of the wreck of the famous excursion steamer, the *Lady Elgin*, is one of the tragic tales of Wisconsin. Three hundred people, largely from Milwaukee, lost their lives on that September night in 1860; their passing inspired a widely sung ballad: "Lost on the Lady Elgin." Here's the way it went:

> Up from the poor man's cottage,
>   Forth from the mansion's door,
>   Reaching across the waters,
>   Echoing 'long the shore . . .

Caught in the morning breezes,
   Borne on the evening gale,
   Cometh a voice of mourning—
   A sad and solemn wail.

Lost on the *Lady Elgin,*
   Sleeping to wake no more;
   Numbered with that three hundred,
   Who failed to reach the shore.

A very sad event, and a sad song. Yet despite the tragedy, the tale of the wreck has a few humorous sidelights. I sang the song one evening to a group of old-timers, and a lady of eighty-seven sang right along with me.

"I was only a baby when the *Elgin* sank," she said, "but I've heard my father tell the story. Do you know that everybody who drowned that night was a *Democrat?* And do you know that the sinking of the *Lady Elgin* broke the Irish rule in Milwaukee?"

They are gathered here before me on my doorstep: a grim little group, leading figures in the tragic tale. From their interwoven lives, I will create the drama of the wreck of the proud *Lady Elgin.* First there is Captain Wilson ... a big man. A sad man. "Tell me your story, Captain!"

"I'm Captain Jack Wilson," he begins. "The *Lady Elgin* was my ship, and I lost her there on that awful night with the Michigan waves rollin' mountain-high in the teeth o' a nor'east gale!

"Aye, she was a proud ship. Named, she was, after Lady Elgin, wife o' the Governor General o' Canada. Pride o'

147

Lake Michigan we called the *Lady Elgin!* Three hundred feet long she was, with twin paddle wheels. But she was a death ship, my boy. A thing o' doom!

"Aye! And even now when the Lake rolls high of a September night, you'll hear my voice whisperin' out o' the mighty rollin' waters:

> Lost on the *Lady Elgin*,
>> Sleeping to wake no more;
>> Numbered with that three hundred,
>> Who failed to reach the shore!"

It was on September 8, 1860, that the *Lady Elgin* met her doom. 1860! The war guns would soon be booming, and men would soon be marching. Union or Disunion! Free or Slave! And here, beside Captain Wilson, is another Captain who failed to make the shore: Captain Barry, of Milwaukee.

"How'd you happen to be aboard the *Lady Elgin*, Captain Barry?"

"It's a curious story, my friend," says the Captain. "It's part of the whole story of where Wisconsin stood in relation to the rest of the Union."

"How's that, Captain?"

"In 1860 Governor Randall, of Wisconsin, and some members of the Wisconsin Legislature were extreme Abolitionists. Threats were made that Wisconsin would secede from the Union unless slavery was abolished. You see, I was Captain of the Union Guards—a mighty proud Milwaukee company—and one day the Adjutant General

148

of the State stopped me and said, 'Barry, in case of war between this State and the United States—in the event we should secede and should take up arms against the Nation—where would you stand?'

"Sir," I replied, "my Guards and I would stand with the United States of America. Any other course would be treason!"

" 'In that case, Barry,' says the Adjutant General, 'we will immediately disband your Company. I order you to give up your arms, and the arms of the Union Guards!' "

"And did you, Captain?"

"I was forced to give up the arms," says the Captain. "But the people *wanted* the Union Guards in Milwaukee. Congressman Larabee tried to get us arms from the United States Government. He failed because we were no longer part of the State Militia. The only course left was for us to purchase our own arms. Congressman Larabee found muskets for us at two dollars apiece!"

"And how did you plan to pay for 'em, Captain?" I asked.

"We planned to pay for them by conducting an excursion to Chicago. I looked around; found an excursion boat that'd take us all from Milwaukee to Chicago and back. The name of that boat was ..."

"It was the *Lady Elgin*, Captain."

Fate played many strange tricks in this famous disaster. In the group before me is an Englishman, a well-known man. Here he is:

SIR HERBERT: I'm Sir Herbert Ingraham, founder and publisher of the *Illustrated London News*. In September 1860, I was visiting the United States. Some of my friends in England said I was making that trip to escape a curse . . . maybe I was; maybe the whole story of the *Lady Elgin* disaster was because of me. You see, many, many centuries ago, there was a Priest of ancient Thebes in Egypt. On his death bed he supposedly said . . .

PRIEST: Place my body in the pyramid of my fathers. And let it be inscribed with my body that whosoever touches my tomb or desecrates my form will be cursed by the triple curse of Isis and Osiris. Let it so be known and written down for all the ages to take warning!

SIR HERBERT: And my father, on a trip to Egypt, assisted in the excavation of the mummy of this very Priest. Yes, and he purchased this very mummy which was sent to the British Museum in London. And one day at the Museum, an Egyptologist examined the body . . .

EGYPTOLOGIST: I found a curious thing, sir, that might interest you: a roll of papyri in the mummy windings. Freely translated it says: "Let a curse destroy him who touches my sacred remains. May his children, and his children's children suffer the fate of untimely death."

SIR HERBERT: And not long afterward my father died, and my younger brother was trampled to death by an elephant while hunting in Somaliland. The curse was working, you see. And while I myself scoffed at the curse, my friends thought—when I took the American journey—that I was running away from my fate.

Well, on September 7, 1860, my wife and I were in the city of Chicago. We wished to journey up the west shore of Lake Michigan, to visit Milwaukee and other points along the way. On the morning of September 7, while I was reading the paper, my wife . . .

LADY INGRAHAM: When do we leave Chicago, Herbert?

SIR HERBERT: It says here, my dear, that an excursion steamer will leave the foot of La Salle Street tonight for Milwaukee and points north. I think we should take that steamer.

LADY INGRAHAM: I'm afraid of those small boats, Herbert.

SIR HERBERT: Nonsense! They aren't small boats! The lake steamers are quite large! Accord-

**151**

ing to the description, this boat is an especially fine one!

LADY INGRAHAM: I can't say I particularly like the idea. But if you think we should go ...

SIR HERBERT: I think we should. Definitely.

LADY INGRAHAM: Very well, dear. What's the name of the boat?

SIR HERBERT: Why ... it's called the *Lady Elgin!*

Here is a couple who loved each other very much. Their name is Eviston. Mr. and Mrs. John Eviston, of Milwaukee. You see, on the evening of September 5, 1860, the Evistons were having supper.

MRS. EVISTON: John ...

EVISTON: Yes, dear ... ?

MRS. EVISTON: John, do you know what day tomorrow is?

EVISTON: Why ... September 6, 1860.

MRS. EVISTON: I mean, what *great* day?

EVISTON: Well, it's not the Fourth of July ... or Washington's birthday. ...

MRS. EVISTON: You've forgotten again! Darling, it's our anniversary!

EVISTON: Why, it is! Sure enough. Let me see, how many is it?

MRS. EVISTON: Oh, don't count them. Every anniversary's been happier than the one before. Darling, do you love me as much as you did last year?

| EVISTON: | I love you more than I did last year. |
| MRS. EVISTON: | I love you more, too. I love you so much it seems nothing in the world could ever separate us. Nothing! |
| EVISTON: | I know. When I think how happy we've been, I believe I could fight and whip the strongest thing in the world! |
| MRS. EVISTON: | John, there's a steamer excursion to Chicago tomorrow. It's been arranged by Captain Barry and the Union Guards. It's to help them raise money to pay for their new muskets. Could we go, John? |
| EVISTON: | Why, I suppose so. Certainly! |
| MRS. EVISTON: | There'll be dancing and singing. We'll have the whole day in Chicago together. |
| EVISTON: | I'll get the tickets first thing in the morning. Say, what boat's making the excursion? |
| MRS. EVISTON: | Captain Wilson's boat. The *Lady Elgin.* She's the best boat on the Lake! Oh, John, I love you so much! |
| EVISTON: | Darling, here's to the happiest anniversary yet! |
| MRS. EVISTON: | Here's to *you*, John! |

And there is one more vignette, arranged by Fate, setting the scene for the disaster. In a dormitory room at Northwestern University at Evanston, Illinois, a slender young fellow, named Edward Spencer, talked with his brother on the evening of September 7, 1860.

"Seems like we never do anything except study any more," said Spencer.

"Sure does, Ed," replied his brother. "This theological course is gettin' me down. We ought to take a holiday. Go for a long hike! Remember how we used to hike along the Mississippi River out home? I'd like to go for a long walk tomorrow—out beyond Winnetka, and right on up the Lake."

"Then let's do it," Spencer said. "Maybe we could stop some place along the Lake and take a swim. I don't get enough swimming any more."

"You used to be the best swimmer along our whole part of the River out home," replied his brother.

"I *was* pretty good. But I'm rusty. Would like to try swimming in Lake Michigan though. Big waves kind of challenge me. Well, tomorrow we'll have an outing!"

"It's a bargain," said the brother.

Now from the vignettes to the proud boat herself. There's the *Lady Elgin's* whistle as she stands at the pier at Milwaukee on the evening of September 6, 1860, a proud, white ship, black smoke funneling out of her stacks; her big paddle wheels beginnin' to churn in their housings.

There's Captain Wilson on the bridge; there's Captain Barry of the Union Guards, looking over his men. There's John Eviston and his wife, arm in arm, there up in the bow! And lined up along the decks are a whole lot of Milwaukee folks, girls and boys, mothers, fathers, kids, grandparents—off for a fine day in Chicago on the pride of the Lakes: the *Lady Elgin!*

"How's the weather, Captain?"

"Weather's fine today," shouts Captain Wilson. *"Ain't* exactly *liked* the feel o' the air, though. Like there might be a storm comin'.

"Cast off there!" he shouts suddenly. "Steady now!"

And there she goes—the *Lady Elgin* off on her trip to Chicago. We won't worry about her on the way down. She had a fine run to Chicago; tied up at the dock on La Salle Street in mighty good time. Yes, the folks from Milwaukee all had a grand time in Chicago that day. They were sightseein'. Captain Barry's Union Guard Company marched through the streets, band playin', and flag wavin'! There was a big banquet that evening, and Captain Barry made a speech.

BARRY: And so, thanks to the loyal support of the people of Milwaukee; and thanks to the excursion on the *Lady Elgin,* the Union Guards have now accumulated enough to pay for the muskets! On behalf of the Guards, I thank you. Thank you all!

There were plenty to cheer Captain Barry's speech. Everybody was having a good time. Nobody knew, or cared, that far up Lake Michigan that evening, was a small lumber schooner, the *Augusta,* heavily laden and wallowing through a lake that was already beginning to turn sullen. On the *Augusta,* the Mate was muttering . . .

155

MATE:    Don't like the look of the sky. Comin' on to storm.
            Storm before midnight sure's shootin'. Have to
            keep a sharp lookout tonight.

And in Chicago, about the same time, the excursion
party heard the whistle of the *Lady Elgin,* and they knew
it was time to get aboard for the return trip to Milwaukee.

There they go up the gangplank—a tired bunch of
holidayers, but a happy bunch, too. And along with those
Irish lads and lassies from Milwaukee are a few new
passengers just getting on at Chicago for the trip up the
Lake. There's F. A. Lumsden, editor of the *New Orleans
Picayune.* He's bumpin' into the Englishman, Sir Herbert
Ingraham.

"Excuse me, sir," says Mr. Lumsden, "didn't go to shove
you. Didn't expect such a crowd!"

"Nor did I," replied Sir Herbert. "Which way are the
rooms?"

"Up thataway, I reckon," says Lumsden, pointing.

"These American boats confuse me."

"I'm Lumsden. *New Orleans Picayune.*"

"Ingraham," says Sir Herbert. He turns to his wife.
"Are you all right, dear?"

"There's such a crowd," replies Lady Ingraham nervously. "Do you think it's safe to go aboard this boat,
Herbert?"

"Certainly, my dear."

"These lake steamers are first class, ma'am," says
Lumsden.

"I've had a strange feeling all day," replies Lady Ingraham, "as though we shouldn't make this trip."

"Nonsense," retorts Sir Herbert.

"Look sharp there!" bawls a voice. "Let the Union Guards through!"

"Here comes that Guard company from Milwaukee," says Lumsden. "Excursionists."

"All right, dear," says Sir Herbert. "Let's try to get through to our cabin. Follow me."

"Herbert, I feel rain on my face," says Lady Ingraham. "We're going to have a storm."

"Won't make a bit of difference. This is a sturdy boat."

"All aboard!" bawls the Captain. "Move sharp there!"

"They're loaded, Captain," answers a voice.

"Then gangplank in!" roars the Captain. "Cast off there!"

"Hawser loose, Captain!"

And there they go, slippin' out into Lake Michigan; a long, white ship, ghostly there in the rain-filled dark; white faces dim along the rails, most of 'em takin' their last look at the Chicago shoreline. Tragedy a long way from the minds of most of 'em too. But up there on the bridge Captain Wilson's anxiously peerin' into the dark, and listenin' to the risin' wind. Captain Wilson's not goin' to be lonely on the bridge tonight. Here come John Eviston and his wife.

"Good evening, Captain Wilson," says Mrs. Eviston.

"Good evening, madam."

**157**

"I'm Mary Eviston, Captain. This is my husband, John."

"Good evening, sir."

"We . . . we wanted to thank you, Captain," says Mrs. Eviston, hesitating a little bit.

"For what, madam?"

"Well," replies Mary Eviston—a little bit embarrassed now—"this is our anniversary, Captain. It's been such a splendid day. We wanted to thank you for a pleasant trip to Chicago. I knew we wouldn't get a chance to say anything when we got to Milwaukee, so . . ."

"You're welcome, I'm sure, madam."

"The *Lady Elgin's* a fine boat, Captain," says John Eviston. "How far are we from Chicago now?"

"Well, sir, we're just about opposite Winnetka, Illinois, now. Lake's roughened up considerable. We won't make such a fast trip back to Milwaukee."

"Just hear the wind," remarks Mary. "And it's so dark on the Lake! Put your arm around me, John dear. I feel cold all of a sudden!"

"We'll go below," says Eviston. They start below but as they go they bump into Lady Ingraham who's comin' up, followed by Sir Herbert.

"Captain, is everything all right?" cries Lady Ingraham.

"Don't mind Lady Ingraham, Captain," says Sir Herbert. "My wife couldn't rest until you'd assured her the trip would be uneventful."

"Everything's shipshape, ma'am. Not a thing to worry about."

"Forgive me, Captain," says Lady Ingraham. "But I'd

158

been upset all day. I started this morning thinking about the Ingraham curse, and I . . ."

"It's nothing," scoffs Sir Herbert. "There's an old story about a curse that's supposed to haunt my family. Something about an Egyptian mummy. It's nothing."

"The wind frightens me," says Lady Ingraham. "Dear! how it's blowing!"

"Ahoy, Captain!" shouts a voice from the bow.

"Ahoy, lookout!"

"Schooner on the port bow, Captain! She's making toward us!"

"How far is she?" bellows the Captain.

" 'Bout three hundred yards."

"Hail her!"

"Ahoy, schooner!" bawls the lookout.

And from out there on the black lake, the answer comes back.

"Ahoy, steamer!"

"You're makin' toward us," bawls the lookout. "Alter course."

"We're trying, steamer!"

"There," says Sir Herbert. "I see the schooner now. I say, she's quite close!"

"Steamer!" comes the bellow over the dark water.

"Schooner?"

"We can't alter course. Sea's too strong!"

"They'll crash us!" cries Lady Ingraham.

"Nonsense," replies Sir Herbert. "There's plenty of room to alter course."

"They'll crash us," cries Lady Ingraham. "I know they'll crash us!"

"Hush, dear," says Mary Eviston. "There's nothing to be alarmed about. Captain Wilson knows what he's doing."

"All the same," says John Eviston, "I don't like the way that schooner rolls. Like there was no steering to her."

"Hard starboard!" shouts Captain Wilson.

"No use, Captain. She's runnin' too high!"

"Keep trying, man! Harder! Harder!"

"I knew we shouldn't have come," sobs Lady Ingraham. "I knew it!"

"Keep calm, old girl. Nothing's happened yet."

"But it will. It will!"

"John," says Mary Eviston, "hold me tight. If anything should happen tonight, we'll stay together, won't we?"

"We'll stay together," says John Eviston. "I'll look after you. Remember what I said yesterday? I love you so much, we're bound to come out all right."

"I remember, John."

"Look sharp, Captain," comes the voice from the bow. "She's comin' down on us!"

"Steamer," bellows the voice from the schooner, "we'll crash you!"

"Can't you pull her over, man?"

"Can't do it, Captain!"

"Then," bellows Captain Wilson, "stand by for crash! Stand by for crash!"

"Herbert! Herbert!" cries Lady Ingraham.

160

"Let me have your hand, John," says Mary Eviston calmly and quietly.

"Here she comes!" roars the Captain. "Get set! Look out! *Now!*"

> *Lost on the* Lady Elgin,
> *Sleeping to wake no more;*
> *Numbered with that three hundred,*
> *Who failed to reach the shore . . .*

And there goes the proud *Lady Elgin* on her last trip: to the bottom of Lake Michigan! As she goes, we hear the cries of women and children. The despairing calling of men who've lost their families in the mad crowd. As she goes she breaks in pieces, and we see people clinging to the wreckage swirled here and there in that wild lake. There's Captain Wilson on a part of the deck with a baby in his arms; there are women there too, and they disappear into the night. There's Sir Herbert Ingraham trying to keep his wife afloat. There's the drummer boy of the Guards. His drum's still strapped to his back and it's keeping him above the water. He's a smart lad. There's Miss Rivers trying to keep her friend Mrs. Walters floating.

Yes, there are heroes aplenty there in that icy water. There's Captain Barry, a good soldier, right to the last he was helping people; and there he goes now, swimming after a woman who's slipped off her bit of wreckage. There's little Willie Pomeroy trying to save his friend Willie Barry. Over there, almost out of sight, is John

O'Neill with Alderman Crilly on another bit of deck. O'Neill is giving his coat to his friend. And there—over there to the right—is John Eviston. Yes, his wife's still with him; they're together holding onto a beam.

They're floating away rapidly, all those who've been able to find wreckage to cling to. Some of 'em will survive. Others'll slip off there in the dark waters. Good luck. Good luck to 'em all!

It's morning now; a mighty grim, lowering morning. The folks on the *Lady Elgin* have been in the water quite a few hours. And down at Northwestern University Edward Spencer and his brother have risen early and are walking along the lake shore.

"Stormy morning," says Spencer. "But I'm glad we decided to come anyway."

"Yeah," replies his brother. "I figured if I studied theology any longer my brain'd bust. Say, Ed, what is that thing lyin' over on the shore there? Part in the water. It looks like a man's body."

"It sure does . . . it *is* a man," shouts Spencer and he begins to run. "He's dead," he says after a minute, kneeling down beside the body. "Been drowned, I guess. There's a board or somethin' here underneath him. Got some printin' on it."

"Yeah," says his brother, taking the board and turning it, *"Lady Elgin."*

"There's been a shipwreck."

"Look, Ed. There's wreckage coming in! There're people out there!"

"They'll never get through the breakers," says Spencer. He begins to unfasten his clothes.

"What are you going to do, Ed?"

"You go and get some help. Get everybody! Lots of ropes and stuff. I'm going out there! I wanted to swim, didn't I?"

A man never knows when he's going to be called on to be a hero. Young Spencer happened to be on the spot, and he could swim. So he jumped in. Almost the first people he saw were the Evistons, John and Mary, still together, holding onto a beam. Mary Eviston was mighty weak.

"Hold on, Mary. We're almost in. Hold on a little longer."

"I can't make it, John," says Mary. "You let me go. Save yourself."

"If we go, we go together. Wait! There's somebody swimmin' out to us! Help!" he shouts. "Over here! Help!"

Well, young Spencer battered his way out to 'em, and he told John he'd help 'em. But they'd have to help *him*, too. And finally he brought 'em in. But you can bet the love John and Mary Eviston had for each other helped. It helped a lot!

Yes, Spencer got his fill of swimming that morning. They tied a rope around his waist, and time after time he went into the Lake. He saved seventeen people. Sometime, if you're ever down around Northwestern University, take a look in the library. You'll see a tablet down there in memory of his bravery. But there were about three hundred souls on the *Elgin* that nobody could save. Among 'em was Captain Wilson.

WILSON: The *Elgin* was my ship, boys. Pride o' the Lakes she was. But she was a death ship. A thing o' doom!

And Captain Barry and the flower of the Union Guards went down. Those muskets did 'em no good. But they were carried by other Milwaukee lads in the Civil War who remembered the *Lady Elgin*, you bet.

Yes sir, and on the Northwestern University grounds, the body of a man was found washed ashore. When they turned him over they said, "This is Sir Herbert Ingraham."

There was a curse on you, Sir Herbert. A curse of old Egypt. You are proof of it. And we wonder: is there Fate in such things? Was it the voice of that ancient Priest of Thebes who caused the wreck of the *Lady Elgin* when he said so many centuries ago, "Let it be inscribed that whosoever desecrates my tomb shall die, and his children, and his children's children."

We don't know. But sometimes of a September night, if we listen hard, we may likely hear the voices of Lake Michigan whisperin' . . .

> Lost on the *Lady Elgin*,
>> Sleeping to wake no more;
>> Numbered with that three hundred,
>> Who failed to reach the shore.

And we will remember the tragic wreck of the proud *Lady Elgin*.

# RAFTSMAN . . .

## on my doorstep

*Oh, a raftsman's life is a wearisome one.*
*It causes many fair maids to weep and mourn.*
*It causes them to weep and mourn*
*For the loss of a true love that never can return.*

Yes, the boys who in the last half of the last century rode the great rafts of logs down the Wisconsin rivers were likely to meet a sad end at almost any time. Rafting was a dangerous business. And probably because the raftsmen were of necessity fearless at their jobs, they were also apt to be boisterous at their play.

**165**

There was one raftsman named Dave Mills who is said to have taken special delight in shooting up the town of Prescott, Wisconsin, which is on the Mississippi River at the junction of the St. Croix—a favorite old-time stopping and assembly place for the raftsmen.

The following yarn uses Dave Mills as a leading character, and might have taken place in Prescott, Wisconsin, in the days just before the Civil War.* The chief conflict, following the best tradition in yarns of this sort, is between Dave Mills, the bad boy, and a Town Marshal of Prescott, whom I'll call Coleman De Witt. It appears that De Witt is mighty sweet on a gal named Lucy, but apparently she isn't so sweet on him.

"Now listen to me, Lucy," says De Witt, "I . . ."

"I'm tired of listenin' to you, Coleman De Witt."

"But Lucy, I want to marry you. I mean it."

"When I marry," says Miss Lucy, "I aim to marry a *man!*"

"Ain't I a man, Lucy?"

"No," Lucy says. "A real man would clean up this town. Especially if he was Marshal like you are. There's not a tougher town in the State. You should be ashamed!"

"It's those raftsmen," says De Witt. "They're a rough lot, and every time they come to Prescott they rip everything apart."

"They certainly do. I'll agree with you there, De Witt," replies Miss Lucy. "Why, look what they did last week.

* A version of this yarn may be found in *A-rafting on the Mississip'*, by Charles E. Russell.

Nailed the beer saloon sign right across the front of the First Presbyterian Church! It's disgraceful!"

"The raftsmen are awful tough," De Witt repeats.

"I don't blame them for wanting to celebrate," says Lucy, "but you ought to keep *order!*"

"It's that Dave Mills. He starts the trouble. Always he's the one starts it!"

Miss Lucy looks at De Witt a minute, then she looks out across the river. "Dave Mills isn't so bad."

"Oh, he *ain't*," cries De Witt. "Well, lemme tell you he's the roughest raftsman on the river. Any river. And he's the best pistol shot too. Every time he gets drunk he snatches that big pistol out and starts shooting things up with it. Why, one of them bullets might as easy hit a feller as not."

"Dave came to see me when he was in town last time," says Miss Lucy.

"Came to see *you?* Dave Mills?"

"He asked me to marry him," says Miss Lucy slowly.

"He *what?*" yells De Witt. "He asked you . . . What did you tell him?" he hollers suddenly.

"Well, I didn't say no."

"Now, Lucy," says De Witt, "you listen to me."

"I'll listen to you, Coleman De Witt," replies Miss Lucy, "when you prove you're as good a man as Dave Mills. Now I'm busy, so goodbye!"

"You'll be sorry, Lucy, if you plays around with that Dave Mills," says De Witt. "That man's chain-lightnin'!"

"I think maybe Dave'll be coming into town today,"

167

says Lucy. She looks off across to the basin where the rafts usually tie up. "Isn't that a big raft tying up now? Maybe that's Dave's raft. Perhaps you should lock him up, Coleman! As if you could," she says laughing, and goes into her house.

"If Dave Mills 's really comin'," mutters De Witt, "then I better go an' warn everybody in town!"

Down at the raft landing, Dave Mills, a tall, bearded young fellow, was singing his favorite song:

> So her Pop says "nay,"
> An' he lopes away,
> An' bobs right back the very next day;
> An' he shuts one eye,
> An' looks very sly,
> So she gives her Pop the sweet goodbye!
> Ohhh, there ain't no cub as sweet as him,
> Handy, dandy, raftsman Jim!

"Mills," hollered another of the rafter boys, "you're feelin' real good! Gonna take Prescott apart again?"

"Mills 's sweet on that there Lucy gal," said another. "You wanter watch out, Mills! Town Marshal 's got his eye on you. Thinks that gal's his'n!"

"Shucks, boys," said Mills, paring his thumbnail with his bowie knife, "I can handle the Marshal. Handle him with one finger."

"Wal, dunno," said a raftsman, "Marshal might be tougher 'n he looks!"

168

"He ain't no wildcat like I am," Mills said.

"Maybe not," said the raftsman. "Anyway, I sure hope they got some o' that Prescott Tanglefoot left. It's mighty potent stuff, though. Wanter be careful you don't spill any on your shoes! Spilled some on mine. Et 'em right down to the soles it did."

"Well," said Dave, slipping his knife into the sheath, "let's go. Wastin' time here. Couple of places I want to visit. Then I'm gonna see my Lucy gal! Gotta let Prescott know I'm here first, though. So strike up 'One-Eyed Riley' and here we go! Look out, Prescott! Yipeee!"

And off they went singin' "One-Eyed Riley."

> He was prime favorite out our way,
> The women folks all loved him dearly;
> He taught the parsons how to pray,
> An' he got their tin, (er pretty nearly).
> He's the man they speak of highly!
> Riddle, liddle, linkum!
> One-Eyed Riley!

And as their singing grew fainter, down in town Coleman De Witt was warning everybody on the street. "Figured you ought to know, Martin," he was saying to the saloonkeeper, "seeing as how you're the biggest saloon and gambling man in town. Dave Mills 'n his rowdies 'll be here real soon!"

"Dave Mills again!" groaned Martin. "Why, it ain't hardly been a month since he took this place apart. I ain't even got the mess cleaned up yet."

**169**

"It's the same with every other saloon in town," said De Witt. "He wrecked 'em all."

"Can't you do something, De Witt?" asked Martin. "After all, you *are Marshal*, and Mills 's gotta be stopped!"

"I'm gonna do somethin'."

"You are? What?"

"You see these things?" said De Witt taking a pair of handcuffs out of his pocket.

"What in the world are them?" asked Martin.

"Handcuffs. Sent fer 'em a long time ago. Guess they're the first ones ever seen in these parts."

"How you gonna use them?"

"I figure to get Dave Mills when he ain't looking," said De Witt grimly, "and then slap 'em on him. Then I aim to take him to jail."

Martin studied for a little bit then he said, "De Witt, people says you're pretty stupid, but maybe you'll amount to something yet. You better go around town now and warn everybody else so's they can keep out of Dave's way. Lordy," he said, wiping his forehead, "it seems like Prescott spends half its time down in the cellars, just keeping away from the raftsmen. Come back here when you tell everybody, De Witt. I'm scared."

"I'll be back," promised De Witt. "I ain't brave, but I got brains aplenty. Brains'll win over Dave Mills. That Mills," he said bitterly, and spit into the street, "had the gall to go and propose to my gal."

" 'Bye, De Witt," Martin said.

Coleman De Witt went on up the Prescott street. When

he got opposite the grocery store he yelled, "Hey there! Mr. Dunbar!"

"Yep!" replied Mr. Dunbar, as the fat little man came quickly to his door. "Who's acalling?"

"Better close up your store, Mr. Dunbar," De Witt said. "Dave Mills 's in town!"

"Oh, good gracious goodness!" cried Mr. Dunbar, popping inside his store and slamming the door. Behind it the heavy bar could be heard falling solidly into place.

De Witt went into the Prescott Hotel. "Broughten! Mrs. Broughten!" he bellowed.

"I hear ye, Coleman De Witt," replied Mrs. Broughten, a plump Irish lady, mother of two pretty lassies, "what'll ye be wantin'?"

"Better close the hotel! Dave Mills 's in town!"

"Lordamercy! Marie! Henrietta!" she called to her two daughters who were working in the kitchen, "pull to the shutters! And you girls, skedaddle for the cellar! Quick!"

When Coleman De Witt got to the First Presbyterian Church he found Parson Richardson working in the little garden around back. "Howdy, Parson," De Witt said to the tall boney preacher.

"How-de-do, my boy," the Parson said, "somethin' I can do for you? Was you wanting to get married for instance, son?"

"Just wanted to tell you, Parson, Dave Mills 's in town."

"Glory be!" Parson shouted, "I'll get my congregation! We'll throw up an earthwork around this church. Thanks for th' warnin', son!"

**171**

"You're welcome, Parson."

"Better stay and help us, young man!"

"I can't, Parson," De Witt said, already on his way. "I've got to go back to Martin's saloon. That's where the tornado'll strike first." He stopped suddenly, listening to the sound of shots, breaking glass, yells, coming apparently from far down the street.

"Better hurry, son," cried the Parson listening too. "Sounds as if your tornado has already struck. That noise is coming from Martin's place, sure's shootin'!"

" 'Bye, Parson," De Witt said, running toward the sounds.

" 'Bye, son," called the Parson, "Lord be with you!"

When De Witt reached the Martin Saloon, the Mills cyclone had already struck and passed on. Pantingly De Witt observed a door hanging by one hinge, fragments of the bar mirror scattered on the floor, tables and chairs hurled into the street. Hearing a groan issue from the rear of the establishment, De Witt investigated and found the legs of the proprietor, Martin, protruding and kicking feebly from the mouth of a great beer barrel. Drawing Martin forth, De Witt asked, though without eagerness, "Which way'd he go?"

"Said he was goin' to Dunbar's grocery," groaned Martin. "Ruint me this time, the rascal! After him, De Witt!"

The men paused a moment as they heard fresh shots and yells farther up the street. "He's up to Dunbar's now. Hurry, De Witt. Hurry!"

172

As De Witt, breaking into a run, neared Mr. Dunbar's store, he heard the grocer screaming, "Thieves! Robbers! Help! Help!"

"Mr. Dunbar," began De Witt, and then stopped; for the entire stock of Dunbar's store was scattered out in the Prescott street.

"This time he's finished me," wailed the grocer. "Just lookut my groceries!"

"I told you to close up!"

"I was closed up! Didn't do no good. He come in here like a cyclone. Busted down my door like it was paper. Coleman De Witt," he said, taking hold of Coleman's coat and emphasizing each word with a tug at the lapels, "you gotta do somethin' about Dave Mills. If you don't arrest that man, you won't be Marshal o' Prescott no longer! Now, git goin'!"

"Well," said De Witt, but not too eagerly, "which way'd he go?"

"Down thataway," screamed Mr. Dunbar. "Down thataway, toward the Widder Broughten's Hotel. Listen! Hear 'em? Hear 'em screamin'? I bet Dave Mills has cornered those poor women in the cellar again."

But the Widder Broughten was far from cornered. She stood, a lioness at bay, on the porch of the hotel, a woodsman's ax raised above her embattled head, and as she screamed her threats she sallied down the steps and drove the last of the Mills marauders fleeing before her. "And don't you dast come back," she cried. "Next time you 'n your river rats come foolin' around my hotel, I'm gonna

**173**

lay somethin' acrost you that ain't gonna be no feather bed!"

"Come on, boys," cried Dave, "let the old cow beller! We'll go down and fix the preacher, then we'll come back here. Maybe the Widder'll change her tune!"

"And maybe you'll catch this ax acrost your noggin'," roared the Widder.

"Ma!" cried her daughter Henrietta from the cellar, "can Marie an' me come out of the cellar now? Has Dave Mills gone?"

"You cannot! You stay there till Coleman De Witt puts that rascal in jail! Here comes De Witt now. De Witt," she said, "you git after that murderin', thievin', good-for-nothin' skunk!"

"Don't look like he done much damage here, Mrs. Broughten."

"No, he didn't. 'Cause I stood here on the front steps and swung Mr. Broughten's ol' ax. Left my mark on a few of 'em, too. Now you go an' git him."

"I'm on my way. Which way'd he go?"

"Down to the Presbyterian Church. Listen! Good heavens! Sounds like a whole battle goin' on down there! I declare . . ."

As De Witt came to the Presbyterian Church, a scene of fearful disorder was disclosed. The Presbyterian congregation, summoned by the Parson, had fought a good fight, but had suffered complete defeat. Groans of the wounded arose from every side. "Parson Richardson," called De Witt, "where are you?"

"Up here, son," said the Parson. "Up here in the tree."

Looking up into the branches of an oak tree, De Witt perceived the Parson hanging from a limb by his coattails which had been securely knotted together. "They've went and nailed the beer sign across the front of the church again," sighed the Parson as the wind swung him back and forth, "but we fought a good fight. The Lord's will be done."

"I'll get you down, Parson."

"Thanks, son. And you put him in jail! Hallelujah!"

"Which way'd Mills go?"

"He run over toward Miss Lucy's house, son. Gal you been courtin'."

"I'm on my way, Parson," said De Witt, as he lifted the Parson to the ground.

"Lord be with you, son. And say, son . . ."

"Yeah?"

"If Dave kills you, I'll preach you a mighty good funeral. 'Bye!"

Dave Mills had arrived at Miss Lucy's house by the time De Witt had helped the Parson out of the tree. Dave was standing outside the house singing another of his favorite songs: "Buffalo Gals."

> I'd like to make that gal my wife,
>> Gal my wife,
>> Gal my wife.
> An' I'd be happy all my life,
> If I had her by me.

Oh, Miss Lucy won't you come out tonight?
Won't you come out tonight?
Won't you come out tonight?
Oh, Miss Lucy won't you come out tonight,
An' dance by the light of the moon!

"Dave Mills," called Miss Lucy, coming out onto the porch, "stop that noise!"

"Come here, Lucy. Wanta talk with ye!"

"Well, what do you want?" said Lucy.

"Want to ask you again. Be my wife, Lucy. I'm big. Strong. Just goin' to waste. Need a woman to steady me down!"

"You're intoxicated!"

"Nope," Dave said, "just feelin' good."

"I heard them yelling down the street," Lucy said. "You've torn up the town again. Dave, why'd you do it?"

" 'Cause I'm the fightin'est, shootin'est, hell-raisin'est rafter boy on the River. Marry me, gal! I'll take ye outta this swamp! Down the River, gal! Down th' ol' Mississip! Down to La Crosse, Prairie du Chien, Quincy, St. Louis! Yeah, clean down to N'Orleans if you want to. I know the River, gal! Th' River 'n me 'n you! Just us three! What you say?"

"It sounds kind of nice," Lucy said, "only you don't mean it. You're drunk."

"I ain't drunk, Lucy. S' help me! Say you'll go with me!"

"I'm kind of promised to Coleman De Witt."

176

"That bean-head! Ha! Why, Lucy, I'll grab aholt of De Witt and wring him out like a sock! Where is he? Won't take me more 'n a minute to settle De Witt!"

"Here comes Coleman now," Miss Lucy said seeing De Witt approaching. "Don't hurt him much, will you, Dave?"

"Why, no, Lucy, I won't hurt him much," Dave said, turning to face De Witt. "Howdy, Bean-Head!" he said to De Witt.

"Dave," said De Witt, keeping his hands in his pockets, "I come to take you to jail."

"Ho! Ho!" roared Mills. "He's come to take me to jail! Well, feller, what're you doin' foolin' around my Lucy gal? Git!"

"I . . . I . . . ain't goin'," De Witt said nervously.

"Then I ain't got no time to dicker," Mills said. "I'll just grab aholt of you, De Witt, an' . . ."

"Wait, Dave," said De Witt, as Mills made a grab for him, "you're bigger 'n me!"

"I'm bigger 'n a thousand of you!"

"But you ain't no stronger 'n me, Mills."

"Huh?" said Mills, sort of surprised by such an outlandish statement.

"I mean it. I got wrists just as big as yours."

"Since when, De Witt? Aw, you're tryin' to put off the leetle trouncin' I got fer you. Stand up to me, De Witt! Take it like a man!"

"Coleman's not a man," said Miss Lucy. "He never grew up."

**177**

"Ho! Ho!" cried Mills. "Hear what the leetle gal thinks o' you?"

"Hold out your wrists, Dave," said De Witt. "Bet they ain't no bigger 'n mine."

"You leetle squirt," yelled Mills, holding out his big wrists, "look at them wrists! Just look at 'em! Them's raftsmen's wrists, boy! Big. Strong. You get them wrists from holding the sweeps in the strong currents. Take a good look, 'cause I'm gonna . . . Hey!" he cried suddenly as De Witt whipped the handcuffs out of his pocket and snapped them on Dave's wrists, "what are them things? Take them things off me!"

"I got ye now," yelled De Witt, dancing around in joy. "I got ye handcuffed! Never heard o' handcuffs, did ye? Well, Lucy, what do ye think of me now? Who's the best man now? Me or Mills?"

"You tricked him," said Miss Lucy. "That's not being a man!"

"But see here, Lucy . . ."

"I hate you Coleman De Witt!"

"Take these things off me, De Witt, you hear?" bellowed Mills.

"You sneakin' trickster, I hate you!" shouted Miss Lucy. "Don't you ever come around here again, Coleman De Witt! Never!" And she ran into the house.

"Lucy," groaned De Witt.

"Take 'em off, De Witt. Take 'em off!" Mills shouted. "I'll whip you with one hand. *One hand!*"

De Witt gazed sadly for a little bit at Miss Lucy's door,

178

then he said, "No. You're goin' to jail, Dave. Git movin'. I'm Marshal o' Prescott, an' my duty comes first. Git!"

The next morning Mr. Martin and Mr. Dunbar met De Witt at the jail. "Coleman," said Mr. Martin, "ye did nice work puttin' Mills in jail. Ain't that right, Dunbar?"

"That's right."

"And as you know, son," continued Mr. Martin, "me bein' the biggest saloonkeeper in Prescott, and Mr. Dunbar bein' the biggest grocer, we got a big interest in seein' that the peace is kept. We congratulate you, De Witt."

"Thanks, Mr. Martin," De Witt said.

"But, boy," Mr. Dunbar said, "me 'n Mr. Martin are worried. Right worried."

"Why? Mills 's locked up, ain't he?"

"Right, son," Martin said, "but see here: what're we gonna do with him? There's the question."

"I know," De Witt said. "It's been worrying me too. This jail ain't none too tight, and sometimes . . . There!" he said as a furious rattling was heard from the interior of the jail, "just listen to him!"

"Let me out!" hollered Dave. "Unlock this here door!"

"You see what I mean?" De Witt said.

"Yep," Martin said, "and if we let him go, he'll travel around and lick everybody in town; probably tear things up again, too!"

"An' if we keep him in *jail*," Dunbar said, "he'll bust the town treasury. Why, I never heard of a man could eat so much! He et up near a quarter of beef for breakfast, not to speak of six loaves of bread, and nigh a barrel o'

179

coffee. Son, Prescott just can't afford to keep a prisoner!"

"We could shoot him," suggested De Witt.

"That don't seem just right neither," said Martin. "This here is a serious problem. Just listen to him sing!"

> So her Pop says "nay,"
> An' he lopes away,
> An' bobs right back the very next day;
> An' he shuts one eye,
> An' looks very sly,
> She gives her Pop the sweet goodbye!
> Ohhh, there ain't no cub as sweet as him,
> Handy, dandy, raftsman Jim!

And as Dave Mills finished his song he called, "Hey there! De Witt! I'm hungry. Bring me some grub!"

"This here is a terrible situation," Martin said. "What *are* we gonna do?"

"I got a little scheme that might work," De Witt said. "Let's make a proposition to Dave."

"What sort o' proposition, son?"

"If we was to put it up to him," De Witt said slowly, "that if he was to fight me to a finish—best man win, you understand—"

"Mills'd whip you in about one second, De Witt."

"Maybe," De Witt said. "Maybe not. I got brains, remember?"

"That's right, son," said Dunbar.

"Let's put it up to him," said De Witt, "that if he whips
180

me he'll be Marshal o' Prescott, and I'll get out. But . . ."

"You mean," said Martin in terror, "you'd saddle us with that rascal as Marshal o' this town? Son, that'd be murder!"

"But if *I* whip him," said De Witt, "he'll leave and never show up here again."

"That wouldn't be no fair fight, son," said Dunbar. "Whew!" he said wiping his face, "Mills, Marshal o' Prescott! Nope. I don't think so."

"I can whip him," De Witt said. "Trust me, boys."

"Too much risk," said Martin.

"We got to let him out sometime," De Witt said, "and when we do . . ."

He was interrupted by a bellow from the prisoner. "Let me out! When I git out I'll hang you fellers to the church. Hang you like chickens!"

"You see?" De Witt continued. "There's no other way."

"If we was just *sure* you'd whip him, De Witt," said Martin, "but heaven help us if you was to lose!"

"This is too big a matter for us three to decide," said Mr. Dunbar. "We ought to have a town meeting and decide."

"A good idea," agreed Mr. Martin. "We *will* call a town meeting. Right now!"

So they went all around the town and got the people together, especially those who'd suffered most from Dave Mills and his pranks. Mr. Martin climbed up on an old stump and started things off by introducing De Witt who told about his proposal.

Then Martin said, "You've heard De Witt's proposition, citizens o' Prescott. Question to be voted on is: Shall De Witt fight Mills, winner to be Marshal o' this town, loser to make himself scarce, never to be seen in these parts again? Mr. Dunbar, how do you vote?"

"With great hesitation," said Mr. Dunbar, "I vote 'yes'!"

"Widder Broughten," said Martin, "how do you vote?"

"I say, let 'em fight!" cried the Widder. "If Mills wins I'll get Mr. Broughten's old ax and settle him myself!"

"Parson Richardson, how will you vote?"

"Let retribution fall upon the sinner's head," yelled the Parson. "It may be that Coleman De Witt is the agent through which vengeance will fall! It's not the way it'd be done back in Connecticut, boys, but let 'em fight! And may the Lord be with our champion!"

"Also with great hesitation and fear," said Mr. Martin, "I will add my vote to the *ayes*, and that makes a majority. So I hereby declare . . ."

He was interrupted in the middle of his sentence by Miss Lucy who came running, jumped up on the stump beside Martin, and cried, "Wait! Wait!"

"Yes, Miss Lucy?" said Martin.

"They can't fight. They mustn't!"

"And why not?"

"Because," said Miss Lucy, "Dave Mills will kill Coleman, that's why!"

"Now, Lucy," said De Witt, "you was wantin' me to prove I was a *man*, weren't you?"

"This . . . this is cold-blooded murder," sobbed Miss Lucy. "Dave Mills has never been beaten."

"Aw," said De Witt, "then you *do* care about me?"

"Well, I don't want you to get killed. Please! Say you won't fight him!"

"I have to fight Dave Mills," De Witt said sternly. "An', Lucy, if I *do* whip him, will you marry me?"

"I don't know. I guess so. But be careful!"

"I'll be careful," said De Witt full of joy at the good news. "He's got brawn, but I got brains. I got a head. Give me a little kiss, Lucy, to sort of seal the bargain?"

"All . . . right, Coleman . . ."

And when the sound of the kiss had faded away, Mr. Martin suggested that the men all go over to the jailhouse to put the proposition to Dave Mills.

Dave began to grin when he heard how things were, and after Mr. Martin finished explainin', Dave said, "You're talkin' my language now, boys. That's a right noble offer. I always did want to be a Town Marshal! I'll really take this place over! But say, De Witt, how'd you ever get up nerve to fight me?"

"I'm gonna whip you, Mills."

"You're a mighty little squirt to be talkin' so big, De Witt. I'll give you a last chance to back down, if you want to crawl!"

"I ain't backin' down."

"Well, it won't be so bad when I'm Marshal," Dave said. "Lucy 'n me'll settle down an' run this town right!"

"Lucy's gonna marry *me*, Dave."

"She say she was?"

"Well," said De Witt, "she sort of did. She said she would if I whipped you."

"Ho! Ho! An' that'll be never! Now let me out of this chicken coop. I got to see Lucy an' get things settled!"

"I told you," said De Witt firmly, "she's gonna marry me!"

"Ain't you forgettin' you got to whip me first? Now I want to see her. Let me out or the whole deal's off!"

"Guess you better let him out, De Witt," Mr. Martin said. "Won't hurt nothin'. Miss Lucy'll tell him off proper."

"All right," said De Witt doubtfully, "but don't you stay long, Mills, and don't start no trouble neither!"

"Why should I start any trouble, De Witt?" said Dave. "Ain't I as good as Town Marshal?"

So a little bit later Dave and Miss Lucy were out on her porch. "Lucy," said Dave, "guess you heard I was gonna fight De Witt."

"Yes, I heard about it."

"De Witt says you'll be *his'n* if he wins."

"Yes."

"'Course you know he ain't gonna win, Miss Lucy."

"I know it. But you'll go easy on him, won't you, Dave? You won't hurt him . . . much?"

"I won't hardly rough him up at all," said Dave. "Just one leetle bounce on the chin'll finish De Witt. Then you'n me'll go down the River, Miss Lucy. Like I said."

184

"Maybe, Dave."

"Give me a leetle kiss on it, Miss Lucy?"

"Well, all right, Dave."

And when the hills along the river had stopped bouncing the sound of the kiss back and forth, Dave said, "I'll be back, Lucy!"

"And I'll be waiting, Dave. For the *winner!*"

Everything was prepared for the tussle. A ring had been drawn on the bare ground, and that was all the preparation they needed, except that Dave Mills and Coleman De Witt had taken off their shirts and were standing, one on each side of the ring. Mr. Martin was acting as the official and he stood in the center of the ring.

He addressed the crowd that was gathered all around. "Now friends," he said, "friends, an' citizens o' Prescott, Wisconsin, it ain't really necessary for me to interduce the pugilists. Here we have Dave Mills—you all know him—the rascal!"

"Howdy, folks," said Dave grinning, "meet your next Marshal!"

"Look at them muscles," Mr. Dunbar said. "Them muscles o' Mills ripple like the ol' Mississip in flood! Parson," he whispered to Parson Richardson who was standing beside him, "you better say a prayer for Coleman De Witt."

"Yes," said the Parson, "I fear Coleman is in for a rough time of it. But the Lord be with him!"

"And here," continued Mr. Martin, "we have Coleman De Witt, Marshal o' Prescott!"

185

After the cheers for De Witt had died down, Widder Broughten whispered to Mr. Dunbar, "My! Coleman looks just like a moltin' rooster!"

"Didn't know Coleman was so skinny," said Mr. Dunbar.

"David against Goliath," yelled the Parson. "Hallelujah!"

"And now," said Mr. Martin, "I will search the contestants for concealed weapons. What's this?" he said, as he stepped over to Dave Mills and slapped him on the thigh. "You got a bowie knife down in your pants!"

"Sure," Dave said, "I always carry that."

"You can't carry it today," Martin said, tossing the knife to a bystander. He stepped over to Coleman De Witt and whispered, "You got anything on you?"

"No," answered De Witt.

"You danged fool," chided Martin. "Here. Take this pair o' brass knuckles!"

"I don't need 'em."

"You danged fool! If he whips you he'll be Marshal! He'll run us all out of town!"

"I'll take care o' him."

"You better!" He went back to the center of the ring. "Now boys, this 's a fight to the finish! Until one or the other hollers 'enough'! When I yell 'go', have at each other. Are you ready? Then go!"

I wish I could describe an epic battle for you. Unfortunately, the climax of the event was over very quickly. Mills took a step into the ring and posed for a moment,

186

his hands up, so that some of the ladies and gents of Prescott could really get an idea of what a fighter looked like. And as Mills stood posing, Coleman De Witt just lowered his head, aimed it for the center of Mills' stomach and rushed across like a torpedo, scoring a hit dead center. There was just the two thumps: one when De Witt's head hit Mills' belly, the other when Mills hit the ground.

"Why," gasped Parson Richardson, "hallelujah! Mills 's down! Git on top o' him, Coleman!"

"Butted Mills in the belly," muttered Mr. Dunbar, just as astonished as could be. "Butted him like a billy goat."

De Witt, who was on top of Mills by this time, had grabbed him by the ears and was flopping his head around and saying, "Say 'enough', Mills! Say it!"

"Enough! Enough!" groaned Mills. "'M' insides is all mixed up!"

There was a terrific cheer and then Mr. Martin took over. "Citizens o' Prescott," he roared, "you just seen our champ, Coleman De Witt, knock the stuffin' out of Dave Mills. True, Coleman hit him in the stomach with the top of his head, but there weren't no rules. The victor, Coleman De Witt! And now," he continued after the cheers had died down, "Dave Mills, git outta town! And don't come back! Never! You hear?"

"I'm goin'," Mills said as he painfully got to his feet and staggered away.

"My boy," Martin said to De Witt, "you said you had a head. We believe you. We all seen you use it today. My boy, you got *brains!*"

Coleman De Witt felt pretty good. He'd saved his town, and he was on his way to claim the prize of victory, Miss Lucy. She was waiting for him too, sitting on her porch, and De Witt didn't even notice she wasn't looking very happy. He just said, "Lucy! I whupped Dave Mills. Now, Lucy, will you marry me?"

"No!" said Miss Lucy, "you coward! You tricked him again! Was that a manly thing to do?"

"Why, I dunno," said De Witt, "there weren't no rules . . ."

"You took advantage of that poor man. Don't you ever come back here again. Never."

"You mean," said De Witt, letting this all soak in, "that you're backing out of your bargain? You ain't gonna marry me?"

"When I marry," said Miss Lucy, "it'll be a *man!*"

"But, Lucy, I'm a . . . ," began De Witt, and then he stopped suddenly and his face got kind of hard and tough. He grabbed Miss Lucy by the arms and held her. "You listen, Lucy," he said, "and I mean listen! Stand still!"

"Quit mauling me! Take your hands off me!"

"You're going to hear me, Lucy. You know what I think of you? I think you're a fickle, two-timing woman! Yes, and I *am* going away, and I ain't coming back! You been stringing me along, Lucy. Goodbye!"

"Why!" said Miss Lucy. She stood still a second, then she got hold of herself and yelled, "Coleman!" and began to chase him down the street.

But the last I heard, she hadn't caught up with him yet.

# SOUNDS . . .

## on my doorstep

I like to listen to the sounds on my doorstep. Sometimes they are far away, as though they were sounds out of the past, or had an understanding of the past. Sometimes they are near by, in the present.

*I hear the sound of wind slowly rising.*

The sound of wind blowing across Wisconsin. In the early days blowing through the great forests, carrying the flocks of wild fowl; driving the flocks of passenger pigeons across the skies; darkening the skies; rippling the waters;

189

scurrying the clouds; driving the rains; hurling the sleet and snow; roughening the lakes; casting the storms upon Wisconsin.

*I hear the wind die to a whisper.*

A gentle breeze around the faces of the free Indians; a quiet breeze stirring the water at the bow of the first white man's canoe: Jean Nicolet, 1634.

Hear the voices in the Wisconsin wind. Lonely voices. The pioneer women were lonely sometimes. Perhaps I'm hearing their voices. There's freedom there, too, though. Freedom. A lot of folks sought freedom in Wisconsin. Found it too. The wind remembers.

*I hear fear in the wind.*

There is fear in the wind. Hear it? A lake storm . . . a boat wrecked on Michigan. The *Lady Elgin,* maybe. Or it's a great storm in the Mississippi Valley. Fear in the wind. But the wind carries other sounds too.

*I hear the sound of a river running.*

There's a good Wisconsin sound. Perhaps I'm hearing the Fox River in the days of Jean Nicolet . . . the River the Indians tell us resembled, in its windings, the track of a pursued fox . . . the River an immense serpent created when it lay down for the night in the vast swamp between the Wisconsin River and the Lake of the Winnebagoes. When the serpent had slept the night it shook itself, and the dew from its back became the water to fill the serpent's bed.

In the river sounds are the songs and the paddle splashings of the *voyageurs* and *couriers de bois;* the songs of the raftsmen and the shanty boys.

The Wisconsin rivers: The Fox, the Wisconsin, the Wolf, the Menominee, the Croix, the Chippewa, the Eau Claire, the Black, the Rock, the Mississippi—main traveled highways.

*I hear cries of joy.*

There's a true Wisconsin sound. I'm hearing the pioneers shouting for joy at new land to break and clear. I'm hearing the sounds of the coming of the mingled peoples of Europe: the '48 men from Germany, swarming into Wisconsin from their revolution-torn country; the Norwegians; the Danes; the Swedes; the Poles; the Finns; the Lithuanians; the Hungarians; the Yugoslavs; the Welsh folk; the Cornish folk; the Scotch folk; the English folk. Those cries mean the Swiss coming to settle at New Glarus. They mean the Southerners coming to settle the lead mining regions in Wisconsin's Southwest. Those cries mean the settlement of this State. New land. Rich land. Free land. New life in heavy hearts. They mean all that. Listen to 'em yell!

Yes, the pioneers. The new settlers. The blood and bone of Wisconsin.

*I hear the sound of faraway drums.*

I'm hearing the mystery drums that sound from some Wisconsin lakes. I'm hearing the strange drum throbbing from Lake Michigan whenever a ship's lost.

I'm hearing Indian drums.

*I hear the sound of a breaking heart.*

Always wondered what a heart sounds like when it breaks. Perhaps I'm hearing Chief Black Hawk's heart breaking when, after the Black Hawk War, most of his people had been killed, and he'd been taken prisoner.

Or it's the sound of Nils Otto Tank's breaking heart when his Moravian Brotherhood Colony left him at Green Bay and went on to re-establish themselves at Ephraim.

Or I'm hearing the breaking heart of Eleazar Williams, Indian missionary, victim of grand delusions. Yes, maybe it's the sound of his heart breaking when, at his death, he must have realized that he simply couldn't make the world believe that he was the Lost Dauphin of France—rightful heir to the French throne.

*I hear the sound of chopping.*

The death knell of the Wisconsin woods: an exciting sound. A sad sound.

*I hear a boat whistle.*

There's the old *Grey Eagle* coming around the bend. She's the fastest river boat on the Mississippi; can run circles around any other boat of her day. She took the first news of the new transatlantic cable to St. Paul.

*I hear the sound of milk hitting the bottom of a pail.*

I like that sound. Milk coming out of the cow's udder and hitting the pail; the first few squirts have a pleasant, ringing sound. That sound tells a Wisconsin story; maybe it's the most important sound in the State. And a friendly sound, too. Picture the milker there on a blizzardy evening, his head against the cow's flank. Mighty warm and cozy.

*I hear the sound of an engine bell.*

That'll be the first train in Wisconsin; over there on the old Milwaukee and Waukesha in 1851.

*I hear the sound of a clock ticking.*

That may be the famous John Muir clock. John Muir became one of our greatest naturalists, but when he was a student at the University of Wisconsin in the early 1860's, he demonstrated his inventive ability. He whittled and carved a wondrous clock that would: 1. collapse Muir's bed at five o'clock each morning; 2. light his lamp; 3. light his fire; 4. open five books for study, and keep each book open for a half-hour interval. Muir said his clock schooled him in discipline and orderly habits.

*I hear the sound of bells across Lake Mendota.*

What I'm hearing is the carrillon tower at the University of Wisconsin. Right pretty. But it's more than just the pleasant sound of bells ringing out a tune. It means an awful lot, that carillon.

It means the formation of the Wisconsin Idea in education. The carrying of the university to the people of the State. It means what a great President of Wisconsin University said years ago—Charles R. Van Hise. He said, "It is the aim of the state university in America to democratize higher education. It is the aim to find the way to the intellectual life of the boy or girl of parts, whatever may be the condition of birth. It is the aim to lend a hand to all the people of this State without respect to age; carrying out to them knowledge which they may assimilate to their benefit. I have confidence to believe that American democracy will take no backward step if the universities with unfaltering courage and steadfast faith, hold to those fundamentals of the university spirit which have justified themselves to the world through their service."

Well, I don't suppose many of the twenty thousand boys and girls at the University of Wisconsin think about it like that. But the sound of those bells ringing out over Lake Mendota will always mean a powerful lot to the people of Wisconsin.